Teacher's Guide and Activity Sheets

For children working towards:

- Year 2 of the NNS *Framework for teaching mathematics* (England)
- Level B of *Mathematics 5 to 14* (Scotland)
- Level 2 of *Lines of Development* (Northern Ireland)

1

Series editor	Peter Clarke
Consultant	Len Frobisher
Writing team	Janine Blinko
	Paula Coombes
	Hilary Koll
	Steve Mills
	Jeanette Mumford

Heinemann Educational Publishers
Halley Court, Jordan Hill, Oxford, OX2 8EJ
a division of Reed Educational and Professional Publishing Ltd
www.heinemann.co.uk

Heinemann is a registered trademark of Reed Educational and Professional Publishing Ltd

First published 2002

05 04 03 02
10, 9, 8, 7, 6, 5, 4, 3, 2

ISBN 0 435 20512 9

Illustrated by Dorian Davies
Designed by Artistix
Cover illustration by Dave Cockburn
Cover design by Paul Goodman
Printed in the UK by Page Bros

Contents

Introduction

Maths Spotlight aims to enable mathematically able children from ages 5 to 11 to develop their understanding of mathematics at a suitably accelerated pace. An emphasis has been given to problem solving and investigational work, to motivate and extend children, whilst fostering a sense of enjoyment in thinking mathematically.

Planning with *Maths Spotlight*

Maths Spotlight 1, intended for use with Year 1 (or P2) children, supports the maths content for Year 2 of the teaching programme in the *Framework for teaching mathematics* (England), Level B of *Mathematics 5 to 14* (Scotland) and Level 2 of *Lines of Development* (Northern Ireland). Although the Teacher's Notes and the Activity Sheets broadly follow the order of the teaching programme in the *Framework*, teachers will be able to 'dip in' to the materials in accordance with their planning documents.

The majority of children in most primary classrooms are likely to be working on the same topic and broad objective(s) in most mathematics lessons. The planning charts on pages 6–16 therefore match the whole-class learning objective(s) for the majority of children in Year 1 (P2) with the specific objective(s) for those working on *Maths Spotlight 1*. These charts will assist teachers to plan a programme of work for their mathematically able children that will run easily alongside their core scheme of work.

The NNS chart has been drawn up so that the first column provides page references to the Supplement of examples in the NNS *Framework* for Year 1 and Year 2 respectively. Further, bold text has been used – in line with the NNS *Framework* – to highlight key objectives. The tint in the chart shows the objectives that are covered in *Maths Spotlight 1*.

Providing challenge for the most able during the daily mathematics lesson

Maths Spotlight incorporates valuable learning opportunities for mathematically able children. These include:

- providing activities that require children to use and apply their knowledge to problem solving or investigations
- encouraging children to make connections between different aspects of mathematics
- promoting thinking skills such as hypothesising, predicting, reasoning
- encouraging initiative and self-direction

Classroom organisation

Maths Spotlight is likely to be of most value during the central part of the daily mathematics lesson, when children are working independently, in pairs or as a group. Where children are being introduced to new concepts, it is recommended that teachers explain the key ideas in more detail. However, topics that extend children's knowledge or ask them to use and apply their existing skills in a problem-solving context require only a small amount of teacher input.

Children's material

Maths Spotlight 1 has 92 Activity Sheets, each designed to provide approximately 15 minutes of work. With the exception of some games, the work can be completed without a high level of teaching input. Any prerequisite skills are listed in the Teacher's Notes. Where it is important for two Activity Sheets on related topics to be completed in a specific order, this is stated in the Teacher's Notes.

Each Activity Sheet contains one or more of the following:

- Practice
  A short practice exercise is normally followed by activities that aim to develop deeper understanding.
- Investigations
  Here children need to use and apply their mathematical knowledge in more open-ended situations. They are encouraged to approach their work in a systematic way and to take responsibility for recording it. Investigations may be done individually, in pairs or as a group.
- Problem solving
  These activities provide opportunities for children to analyse, then solve problems and to reflect on alternative methods that could be used.
- Games
  Paired or small group games allow children to use and apply their knowledge in an interesting and enjoyable way. They provide opportunities for children to think creatively and to make links between related aspects of mathematics. Most of the games use readily available classroom resources.

Teacher's Guide

Each Activity Sheet is supported by full Teacher's Notes, including answers.

Strand and Topic from NNS *Framework for teaching Mathematics*

Objective from the NNS *Framework*

Key mathematical words

Equipment needed

Prerequisite knowledge or experience for children

Possible difficulties and ways to resolve them

Suggested teaching input

Possible questions to encourage children to verbalise their reasoning. These may help with informal assessment.

Activity Sheet answers

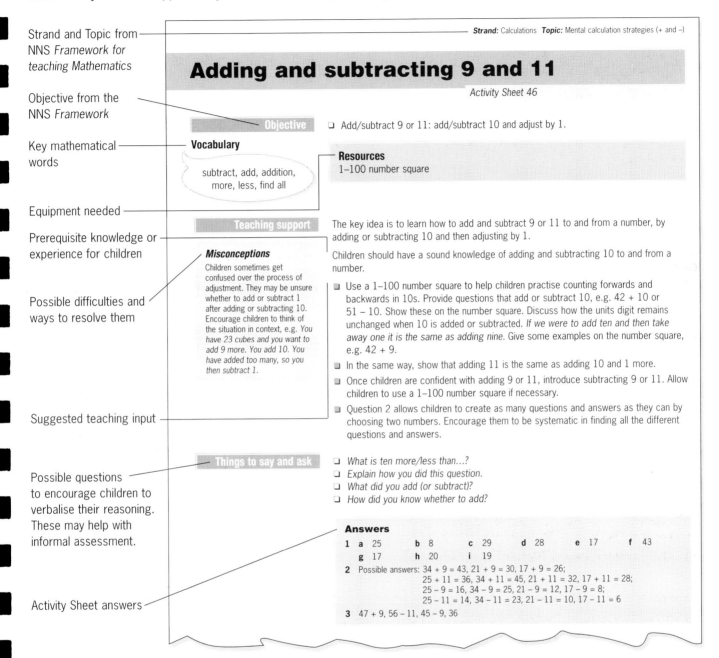

Strand: Calculations **Topic:** Mental calculation strategies (+ and –)

Adding and subtracting 9 and 11

Activity Sheet 46

Objective

❑ Add/subtract 9 or 11: add/subtract 10 and adjust by 1.

Vocabulary

subtract, add, addition, more, less, find all

Resources
1–100 number square

Teaching support

Misconceptions

Children sometimes get confused over the process of adjustment. They may be unsure whether to add or subtract 1 after adding or subtracting 10. Encourage children to think of the situation in context, e.g. *You have 23 cubes and you want to add 9 more. You add 10. You have added too many, so you then subtract 1.*

The key idea is to learn how to add and subtract 9 or 11 to and from a number, by adding or subtracting 10 and then adjusting by 1.

Children should have a sound knowledge of adding and subtracting 10 to and from a number.

▪ Use a 1–100 number square to help children practise counting forwards and backwards in 10s. Provide questions that add or subtract 10, e.g. 42 + 10 or 51 – 10. Show these on the number square. Discuss how the units digit remains unchanged when 10 is added or subtracted. *If we were to add ten and then take away one it is the same as adding nine.* Give some examples on the number square, e.g. 42 + 9.

▪ In the same way, show that adding 11 is the same as adding 10 and 1 more.

▪ Once children are confident with adding 9 or 11, introduce subtracting 9 or 11. Allow children to use a 1–100 number square if necessary.

▪ Question 2 allows children to create as many questions and answers as they can by choosing two numbers. Encourage them to be systematic in finding all the different questions and answers.

Things to say and ask

❑ *What is ten more/less than...?*
❑ *Explain how you did this question.*
❑ *What did you add (or subtract)?*
❑ *How did you know whether to add?*

Answers

1 a 25 **b** 8 **c** 29 **d** 28 **e** 17 **f** 43
g 17 **h** 20 **i** 19
2 Possible answers: 34 + 9 = 43, 21 + 9 = 30, 17 + 9 = 26;
25 + 11 = 36, 34 + 11 = 45, 21 + 11 = 32, 17 + 11 = 28;
25 – 9 = 16, 34 – 9 = 25, 21 – 9 = 12, 17 – 9 = 8;
25 – 11 = 14, 34 – 11 = 23, 21 – 11 = 10, 17 – 11 = 6
3 47 + 9, 56 – 11, 45 – 9, 36

Spotlight 1 and the NNS *Framework*

NNS *Framework* page (Y1/Y2)	Objective for Year 1	Objective for Year 2	Teacher's Guide page	Activity Sheet number
NUMBERS AND THE NUMBER SYSTEM				
Counting, properties of numbers and number sequences				
2 / 3	Know the number names and recite them in order to at least 20, from and back to zero.	Say the number names in order to at least 100, from and back to zero.	18	1
2 / 3	**Count reliably at least 20 objects.**	Count reliably up to 100 objects by grouping them: for example, in tens, then in fives or twos.	18	2
2 / 3	**Describe and extend number sequences:** **– count on and back in ones from any small number, and in tens from and back to zero.**	**Describe and extend simple number sequences:** **– count on or back in ones or tens, starting from any two-digit number.**	18, 19, 20	1, 3, 4
		Describe and extend simple number sequences: – count in hundreds from and back to zero.	21	5
4 / 5	Describe and extend number sequences: – count on in twos from zero, then one, and begin to recognise odd or even numbers to about 20 as 'every other number'.	Describe and extend simple number sequences: – count on in twos from and back to zero or any small number, and **recognise odd and even numbers** to at least 30.	22, 28	6, 13, 7
6 / 7	Describe and extend number sequences: – count in steps of 5 from zero to 20 or more, then back again; begin to count on in steps of 3 from zero.	Describe and extend simple number sequences: – count on in steps of 3, 4 or 5 to at least 30, from and back to zero, then from and back to any given small number.	23, 24, 27, 28	8, 9, 12, 13
– / 7		Begin to recognise two-digit multiples of 2, 5 or 10.	22, 25, 26	7, 10, 11
Place value and ordering				
8 / 9	**Read and write numerals from 0 to at least 20**	**Read and write whole numbers to at least 100** in figures and words.	18, 19, 29	1, 3, 15
8 / 9	Begin to know what each digit in a two-digit number represents. Partition a 'teens' number and begin to partition larger two-digit numbers into a multiple of 10 and ones (TU).	**Know what each digit in a two-digit number represents, including 0 as a place holder**, and partition two-digit numbers into a multiple of ten and ones (TU).	30, 31, 36	16, 17, 22, 23
10 / 11	**Understand and use the vocabulary of comparing and ordering numbers,** including ordinal numbers to at least 20.	Use and begin to read the vocabulary of comparing and ordering numbers, including ordinal numbers to 100.	32	18
	Use the = sign to represent equality.	Use the = sign to represent equality.	31	17
	Compare two familiar numbers, say which is more or less, and give a number which lies between them.	Compare two given two-digit numbers, say which is more or less, and give a number which lies between them.	33	19
12 / 13	**Within the range 0 to 30, say the number that is 1 or 10 more or less than any given number.**	Say the number that is 1 or 10 more or less than any given two-digit number.	34, 35	20, 21

NNS *Framework* page (Y1/Y2)	Objective for Year 1	Objective for Year 2	Teacher's Guide page	Activity Sheet number
14 / 15	**Order numbers to at least 20**, and position them on a number track.	**Order whole numbers to at least 100,** and position them on a number line and 100 square.	36	22, 23
Estimating and rounding				
16 / 17	Understand and use the vocabulary of estimation.	Use and begin to read the vocabulary of estimation and approximation.	37, 38	24, 25
	Give a sensible estimate of a number of objects that can be checked by counting.	Give a sensible estimate of at least 50 objects.	37, 38	24, 25
– / 19		Round numbers less than 100 to the nearest 10.	39	26
Fractions				
– / 21, 23		Begin to recognise and find one half and one quarter of shapes and small numbers of objects.	40, 41	27, 28, 29, 30
		Begin to recognise that two halves or four quarters make one whole and that two quarters and one half are equivalent.	42, 43, 44	31, 32, 33, 34
CALCULATIONS				
Understanding addition and subtraction				
24 / 25	**Understand the operation of addition and use the related vocabulary.**	Extend understanding of the operation of addition.	45	35
		Use and begin to read the related vocabulary.	45	35
	Begin to use the +, – and = signs to record mental calculations in a number sentence, and to recognise the use of symbols such as ❏ or △ to stand for an unknown number.	Use the + and = signs to record mental additions in a number sentence, and recognise the use of a symbol such as ❏ or △ to stand for an unknown number.	45, 46, 49	35, 36, 39
	Begin to recognise that addition can be done in any order.	Recognise that addition can be done in any order, but not subtraction: for example, 3 + 21 = 21 + 3, but 21 – 3 does not equal 3 – 21.	49	39
		Understand that subtraction is the inverse of addition (subtraction reverses addition).		
26 / 27	Begin to recognise that more than two numbers can be added together.	Understand that more than two numbers can be added.	47	37
		Begin to add three single-digit numbers mentally (totals up to about 20) or three two-digit numbers with the help of apparatus (totals up to 100).	47	37
28 / 29	**Understand the operation of subtraction (as 'take away', 'difference', and 'how many more to make'), and use the related vocabulary.**	Extend understanding of the operation of subtraction. Use and begin to read the related vocabulary.	52 / 52, 54	42 / 42, 44
	Begin to use the – and = signs to record mental calculations in a number sentence, and to recognise the use of symbols such as ❏ or △ to stand for an unknown number.	Use the – and = signs to record mental subtractions in a number sentence, and recognise the use of a symbol such as ❏ or △ to stand for an unknown number.	53, 54	43, 44
		Understand that subtraction is the **inverse of addition** (subtraction reverses addition).	52	42

NNS *Framework* page (Y1/Y2)	Objective for Year 1	Objective for Year 2	Teacher's Guide page	Activity Sheet number
Rapid recall of addition and subtraction facts				
30 / 31	**Know by heart:** **– all pairs of numbers with a total of 10**; – addition facts for all pairs of numbers with a total up to at least 5, and the corresponding subtraction facts; – addition doubles of all numbers to at least 5 Begin to know: – addition facts for all pairs of numbers with a total up to at least 10, and the corresponding subtraction facts.	**Know by heart:** **– all addition and subtraction facts for each number to at least 10;** – all pairs of numbers with a total of 20; – all pairs of multiples of 10 with a total of 100.	45, 51	35, 41
32 / 33	Use knowledge that addition can be done in any order to do mental calculations more efficiently. For example: – put the larger number first and count on in ones, including beyond 10; – begin to partition into '5 and a bit' when adding 6, 7, 8 or 9, then recombine.	**Use knowledge that addition can be done in any order to do mental calculations more efficiently.** For example: – put the larger number first and count on in tens or ones; – add three small numbers by putting the largest number first and/or find a pair totalling 10; – partition into '5 and a bit' when adding 6, 7, 8 or 9, then recombine; – partition additions into tens and units, then recombine.	45 50	35 40
32 / 33		Find a small difference by counting up from the smaller to the larger number.	55	45
Mental calculation strategies (+ and –)				
32 / 33	Identify near doubles, using doubles already known.	Identify near doubles, using doubles already known.	48	38
34 / 35	Add 9 to single-digit numbers by adding 10 then subtracting 1.	Add/subtract 9 or 11: add/subtract 10 and adjust by 1. Begin to add/subtract 19 or 21: add/subtract 20 and adjust by 1.	56 57	46 47
34 / 35	Use patterns of similar calculations.	Use patterns of similar calculations.	48	38
34 / 35		**State the subtraction corresponding to a given addition, and vice versa.**	58	48
36, 38 / 37, 39	Use known number facts and place value to add or subtract a pair of numbers mentally within the range 0 to at least 10, then 0 to at least 20.	Use known number facts and place value to add/subtract mentally.	59, 60	49, 50
40 / 41	Begin to bridge through 10, and later 20, when adding a single-digit number.	Bridge through 10 or 20, then adjust.	60	50
Understanding multiplication and division				
– / 47		**Understand the operation of multiplication as repeated addition or as describing an array.**	66, 67	55, 56
		Use and begin to read the related vocabulary.	66, 67	55, 56

NNS *Framework* page (Y1/Y2)	Objective for Year 1	Objective for Year 2	Teacher's Guide page	Activity Sheet number
		Use the × and = signs to record mental calculations in a number sentence, and recognise the use of a symbol such as ❑ or △ to stand for an unknown number.	66 68	55 57
		Know and use halving as the inverse of doubling.	69	58
– / 49		Begin to understand division as grouping (repeated subtraction) or sharing. Use and begin to read the related Vocabulary.	70, 71	59, 60
		Use the ÷ and = signs to record mental calculations in a number sentence, and recognise the use of a symbol such as ❑ or △ to stand for an unknown number.	70, 71 72	59, 60 61
		Know and use halving as the inverse of doubling.	70, 71	59, 60
Rapid recall of multiplication and division facts				
– / 53		**Know by heart: – multiplication facts for the 2 and 10 times-tables;** – doubles of all number to 10 and the corresponding halves.	68 69	57 58
		Begin to know multiplication facts for the 5 times table. Derive quickly: – division facts corresponding to the 2 and 10 times-tables.	72	61
– / 53		Know by heart: – doubles of all number to 10 and the corresponding halves. Derive quickly: – doubles of all numbers to at least 15; – doubles of multiples of 5 to 50; – halves of multiples of 10 to 100.	73	62
Mental calculations strategies (× and ÷)				
– / 57		Use known number facts and place value to carry out mentally simple multiplications and divisions.		
Checking results of calculations				
– / 59		Repeat addition in a different order.	59	49
– / 59		**Check with an equivalent calculation.**	55	45
SOLVING PROBLEMS				
Making decisions				
60 / 61	Choose and use appropriate number operations and mental strategies to solve problems.	**Choose and use appropriate operations and efficient calculation strategies to solve problems.**	46, 47, 48, 50, 53, 54, 87	36, 37, 38, 40, 43, 44, 77

NNS *Framework* page (Y1/Y2)	Objective for Year 1	Objective for Year 2	Teacher's Guide page	Activity Sheet number
Reasoning about numbers or shapes				
62 / 63	Solve simple mathematical problems or puzzles; recognise and predict from simple patterns and relationships. Suggest extensions by asking 'What if...?' or 'What could I try next?'	Solve mathematical problems or puzzles, recognise simple patterns and relationships, generalise and predict. Suggest extensions by asking 'What if...?' or 'What could I try next?'	27, 47, 48, 60, 64, 65, 94	12, 37, 38, 50, 53, 54, 84
64 / 65	Investigate a general statement about familiar numbers or shapes by finding examples that satisfy it.	Investigate a general statement about familiar numbers or shapes by finding examples that satisfy it.	26, 25, 28, 49, 94, 99 29, 46, 94	11, 10, 13, 39, 85, 91 14, 36, 84, 85
64 / 65	Explain methods and reasoning orally.	**Explain how a problem was solved** orally and, where appropriate, in writing.		
Problems involving 'real life', money or measures				
66 / 67	**Use mental strategies to solve simple problems** set in 'real life' contexts, **using counting, addition, subtraction, halving or doubling, explaining methods and reasoning orally.**	Use mental addition and subtraction, simple multiplication and division, to solve simple word problems involving numbers in real life', using one or two steps.	46, 54, 55, 62, 68, 72, 87 87	36, 44, 45, 51, 57, 61, 77 77
68 / 69	Recognise coins of different values.	Explain how the problem was solved. Recognise all coins and begin to use £.p notation for money.	63, 64, 65	52, 53, 54
	Find totals and change from up to 20p.	Find totals, give change, and work out which coins to pay.	63, 64, 65	52, 53, 54
	Work out how to pay an exact sum using smaller coins.			
68 / 69	**Use mental strategies to solve simple problems** set in money contexts, **using counting, addition, subtraction, halving or doubling, explaining methods and reasoning orally.**	Use mental addition and subtraction, simple multiplication and division, to solve simple word problems involving numbers in money, using one or two steps.	50 86 86	40 76 76
70 / 71	**Use mental strategies to solve simple problems** set in measurement contexts, **using counting, addition, subtraction, halving or doubling, explaining methods and reasoning orally.**	Explain how the problem was solved. Use mental addition and subtraction, simple multiplication and division, to solve simple word problems involving numbers in measures, using one or two steps. Explain how the problem was solved.	83, 84, 85, 85	72, 73, 74, 75
MEASURES, SHAPE AND SPACE				
72 / 73	**Understand and use the vocabulary related to length, mass and capacity.**	Use and begin to read the vocabulary related to length, mass and capacity.	74, 76, 78	63, 65, 67
72 / 73	Compare two lengths, masses or capacities by direct comparison; **extend to more than two.**	**Estimate, measure and compare lengths, masses and capacities, using standard units** (m, cm, kg, litre).	74, 76, 78	63, 65, 67
	Measure using uniform non-standard units or standard units.			
74 / 75	**Suggest suitable standard or uniform non-standard units and measuring equipment to estimate, then measure, a length, mass or capacity,** recording estimates and measurements as 'about 3 beakers full' or 'about as heavy as 20 cubes'.	**Suggest suitable units and equipment for such measurements.**	74, 76, 78	63, 65, 67

NNS *Framework* page (Y1/Y2)	Objective for Year 1	Objective for Year 2	Teacher's Guide page	Activity Sheet number
76 / 77		**Read a simple scale to the nearest labelled division, including using a ruler to draw and measure lines to the nearest centimetre**, recording estimates and measurements as '3 and a bit metres long' or 'about 8 centimetres' or 'nearly 3 kilograms heavy'.	75, 77, 79	64, 66, 68
78 / 79	Understand and use the vocabulary related to time.	Use and begin to read the vocabulary related to time.	80	69
		Use units of time and know the relationships between them (second, minute, hour, day, week).	80	69
		Suggest suitable units to estimate or measure time.	80	69
	Order familiar events in time.			
	Know the days of the week and the seasons of the year.	Order the months of the year.	81	70
	Read the time to the hour or half hour on analogue clocks.	Read the time to the hour, half hour or quarter hour on an analogue clock and a 12-hour digital clock, and understand the notation 7:30.	82	71
Shape and space				
80 / 81	**Use everyday language to describe features of familiar 3-D and 2-D shapes**, including the cube, cuboid, sphere, cylinder, cone…, circle, triangle, square, rectangle…, referring to properties such as the shapes of flat faces, or the number of faces or corners… or the number and types of sides.	**Use the mathematical names for common 3-D and 2-D shapes**, including the pyramid, cylinder, pentagon, hexagon, octagon…	88 89	78 79
		Sort shapes and describe some of their features, such as the number of sides and corners, symmetry (2-D shapes), or the shapes of faces and number of faces, edges and corners (3-D shapes).	88 89	78 79
82 / 83	Make and describe models, patterns and pictures using construction kits, everyday materials, Plasticine…	Make and describe shapes, pictures and patterns using, for example, solid shapes, templates, pinboard and elastic bands, squared paper, a programmable robot…	88 89	78 79
	Begin to relate solid shapes to pictures of them.	Relate solid shapes to pictures of them.	89	79
84 / 85	Fold shapes in half, then make them into symmetrical patterns.	Begin to recognise line symmetry.	90	80
86 / 87	Use everyday language to describe position, direction and movement.	**Use mathematical vocabulary to describe position, direction and movement**: for example, describe, place, tick, draw or visualise objects in given positions.	91	81

NNS *Framework* page (Y1/Y2)	Objective for Year 1	Objective for Year 2	Teacher's Guide page	Activity Sheet number
88 / 89	Talk about things that turn. Make whole turns and half turns.	Recognise whole, half and quarter turns, to the left or right, clockwise or anti-clockwise.	92	82
		Know that a right angle is a measure of a quarter turn, and recognise right angles in squares and rectangles.	92	82
	Use one or more shapes to make, describe and continue repeating patterns…	Give instructions for moving along a route in straight lines and round right-angled corners.	93	83
HANDLING DATA				
Organising and using data				
90, 92 / 91, 93	Solve a given problem by sorting, classifying and organising information in simple ways, such as: – using objects or pictures; – in a list or simple table. Discuss and explain results.	Solve a given problem by sorting, classifying and organising information in simple ways, such as: – in a list or simple table; – in a pictogram; – in a block graph. Discuss and explain results.	95, 97, 99 96 97, 98 100 96, 97, 100	86, 88, 91 87 89, 90 92 87, 88, 92

Spotlight 1 and Mathematics 5 to 14 (Scotland)

Target for Level B	Teacher's Guide page	Activity Sheet number
NUMBER MONEY AND MEASUREMENT		
Range and type of numbers		
Work with: – whole numbers up to 100 and then up to 1000 – quarters	18, 21, 29, 30, 31, 32, 33, 34, 35, 36, 37, 38 40, 41, 42, 43	1, 2, 5, 15, 16, 17, 18, 19, 20, 21, 22, 23, 24, 25 27, 28, 29, 30, 31, 32
Money		
Use coins up to £1 including exchange	62, 63, 64	52, 53, 54
Add and subtract		
Add and subtract: – mentally for numbers 0 to 20; in some cases beyond 20 – without a calculator for 2 digit numbers – with a calculator for 2 digit numbers – with a calculator for numbers to 2 digits added to or subtracted from 3 digits – in applications in number, measurement and money, including payments and change up to £	45, 46, 47, 48, 53, 54, 58, 59, 60 49, 51, 52, 55, 56, 57 50, 62, 63, 64, 65, 83, 86	35, 36, 37, 38, 43, 44, 48, 49, 50 39, 41, 42, 45, 46, 47 40, 51, 52, 53, 54, 72, 76
Multiply and divide:		
Multiply and divide: – mentally by 2, 3, 4, 5, 10, within the confines of these tables – without a calculator for 2 digit numbers multiplied by 2, 3, 4, 5, 10 – with a calculator for 2 digit numbers multiplied and divided by any digit – in applications in number, measurement and money to £1	66, 67, 68, 69, 70, 71, 72 73	55, 56, 57, 58, 59, 60, 61 62
Round numbers		
Round 2 digit whole numbers to the nearest ten	39	26
Fractions, percentages and ratio		
Find halves and quarters of quantities involving 1- or 2-digit numbers	40, 41, 42, 43, 44	27, 28, 29, 30, 31, 32, 33, 34
Patterns and sequences		
Work with patterns and sequences: – even and odd numbers – whole number sequences within 100 – more complex sequences with shapes	22, 26, 28, 29 19, 20, 21, 23, 24, 25, 27	6, 7, 11, 13, 14 3, 4, 5, 8, 9, 10, 12
Functions and equations		
Find the missing numbers in statements where symbols are used for unknown numbers or operators	46, 54	36, 44
Measure and estimate		
Measure in easily handled standard units and fractions of them: – length, weight – place sets of objects in order of length or weight – use the abbreviations m, cm and equivalences Realise that length can be conserved when shape changes Read scales on measuring devices to the nearest graduation	74, 75 74, 75	63, 64 63, 64

13

Target for Level B	Teacher's Guide Page	Activity Sheet Number
Time		
Work with time: – place events in time sequences – tell time using analogue displays; and the terms "quarter past / to, half past" – read time in hours and minutes using digital displays	80, 81 82, 85 82, 85	69, 70 71, 75 71, 75
SHAPE, POSITION AND MOVEMENT		
Range of shapes		
Collect, discuss, make and use 3D and 2D shapes: – respond to descriptions which refer to features of shapes – identify and name triangular prism, square pyramid – find shapes that will tile and continue tilings using grids or tiles – make 3D shapes from diagrams or pictures	89, 94	79, 84, 85
Position and movement		
Discuss position and movement: – give and understand instructions for turning through right angles – recognise and name the four compass points – use grid references to read or plot location on grid – give or follow directions to create a square or rectangle	92 91, 93	82 81, 83
Symmetry		
Work with symmetry: – recognise symmetrical shapes by folding or using a mirror	90	80
Angle		
Angles: – use a template to draw or check for a right angle		
INFORMATION HANDLING		
Collect		
By obtaining information for a task from sets of pictures or diagrams By conducting a class survey	97, 100	88, 89, 92
Organise		
By using a tally sheet with individual ticks for each item By using a simple database in which the teacher defines the headings or fields	97	88
Display		
By using tables, charts or diagrams, such as mapping one to many By constructing a bar graph	96, 97, 98 100	87,89, 90 92
Interpret		
From displays by asking specific questions	96, 97, 90, 99, 100	87, 88, 89, 90, 91, 92

Spotlight 1 and Lines of Development (Northern Ireland)

Level	Level description	Teacher's Guide page	Activity Sheet number
M2.1	Appreciate the conservation of length/weight through practical experience.		
M2.2	Experiment with a variety of containers in order to find those which hold the same amount.		
M2.3	Use arbitrary units for measuring and comparing lengths, weighing objects and measuring capacity. Measure distance (using many identical units; using two identical units) Measure capacity (same unit; same container different units)		
M2.4	Compare the size of two objects whose volume is clearly different, e.g. blocks, dice. Order three or more objects with respect to volume.	79	68
M2.5	Use parts of the body to measure lengths.		
M2.6	Appreciate the need for a standard unit of length, weight and capacity.	74, 75, 76, 77, 78, 79	63, 64, 65, 66, 67, 68
A2.1	Cover surfaces using non-standard unit shapes which leave gaps; do not leave gaps.		
T2.1	Use a variety of arbitrary units to measure time, e.g. egg timer, water clock, hand-claps.		
T2.2	Recognise special times on the clock face.	82	71
T2.3	Know, through sequencing: days of the week; months of the year; seasons.	81	70
T2.4	Become familiar with the 12 hour clock – language and representation – leading on to telling the time: in hours; in half hours	80, 82	69, 71
HD2.1	Record, compare and interpret data which represents people/objects using: drawings or pictures; gummed paper shapes.		
HD2.2	Sort people/objects for 2 criteria on diagrams such as Tree, Venn or Carroll. Respond to questions about resulting displays.	99	91
HD2.3	Represent pictorially and discuss the result of sorting for 2 criteria using given Tree, Venn and Carroll diagrams.		
HD2.4	Collect information relevant to a topic and record in a given table.	95, 96, 97	86, 87, 88
HD2.5	Organise and discuss the recording of data in: pictograms; simple block graphs Introduce use of baseline (horizontal and vertical). Discuss appropriate title and labels.	97, 98, 100	89, 90, 92
HD2.6	Represent data from a frequency table on a block graph. Interpret results.		
N2.1	Develop an understanding of the commutative property of addition.	45, 47, 49, 59	35, 37, 39, 49
N2.2	Explore addition and subtraction to appreciate their relationship.	52, 58	42, 48
N2.3	Explore numbers to 20: count orally; write numerals; make sets, recognize the spoken number and associated symbols.	18, 51	1, 41
N2.4	Numbers 11–15/11–20: add using materials/number line; explore number stories in a variety of ways; be aware of 10 being an important number; estimate numbers up to 15, 20.	29, 37, 45, 47, 51	14, 24, 25, 35, 37, 40
N2.5	Subtract within 20: use materials/number line to take away and find the difference.	51, 53, 55	40, 43, 45
N2.6	Add mentally with total no greater than 20: (i) 1 or 2 to any number; (ii) on to add 10 to any number; (iii) doubles and near doubles.	34, 35, 48, 69	20, 21, 38, 58
N2.7	Carry out simple shopping activities within 10p requiring no change using: (i) 1p and 2p coins; (ii) 1p, 2p and 5p coins.		
N2.8	Subtract mentally within 20: (i) 1 or 2 from any number; (ii) 10 from any number.	34, 35	20, 21
N2.9	Extend number to 50/100: (i) count orally; (ii) from a given number count on/back; (iii) explore numbers in a variety of ways; (iv) recognize numerals in spoken and written form.	18, 19, 21, 29	1, 2, 3, 5, 15
N2.10	Establish the relationships between coins up to 10p.	50	40

Level	Level description	Teacher's Guide page	Activity Sheet number
N2.11	Prepare for place value: (i) investigate and discuss numbers through grouping and exchanging activities to at least 50; (ii) order numbers; (iii) use 1–50 grid/100 square, abacus, base 10 materials to explore the composition of numbers to 50/100 as tens and units; (iv) appreciate the position of the tens digits indicates its value.	30, 31, 32, 33, 34, 35, 36	16, 17, 18, 19, 20, 21, 22, 23
N2.12	Carry out shopping activities and games requiring change out of: (i) 10p; (ii)15p.	50	40
N2.13	Extend the concept of place value: explore the idea of exchange using base 10 material.		
N2.14	Recognise 20p and 50p coins and establish relationships with all coins up to 50p.	63	52
N2.15	Explore addition using a 1–50 grid/100 square: without 'bridging' the 10; with 'bridging' the 10.	49, 59, 60	39, 49, 50
N2.16	Explore extended addition using 100 square.	23, 24, 25, 12	8, 9, 10, 12
N2.17	Carry out shopping activites and games to build up confidence using a range of coins up to 50p.	64	53
N2.18	Explore subtraction using a 1–50 grid/100 square: (i) without 'bridging' the 10; (ii) with 'bridging' the 10.		
N2.19	Use 1–50 grid/100 squares to explore adding: (i) 10 and multiples of 10; (ii) 11,21; (iii) 9,19.	52, 56, 57	41, 46, 47
N2.20	Use 100 square to develop personal methods for adding any 2 digit numbers: record horizontally.	62, 83, 84, 85, 87, 88	51, 72, 73, 74, 76, 77
N2.21	Use 1–50 grid/100 squares to explore subtraction: 10 and multiples of 10; 11,21; 9,19.	56, 57	46, 47
N2.22	Explore addition using a variety of practical apparatus , e.g. abacus, base 10, games and calculator; present results orally and in written form.	47, 50	37, 40
N2.23	Establish relationships between all coins up to £1.	64	53
N2.24	Use personal methods to subtract from a 2-digit number: (i) a single digit; (ii) a 2-digit number; (iii) record horizontally.	62, 83, 87, 88	51, 72, 76, 77
N2.25	Develop vertical addition through formal recording: totalling 50,99; estimate answers to nearest 10 before calculating.		
N2.26	Carry out shopping activities with money values up to £1: (i) no change; (ii) with change.	64, 65	53, 54
N2.27	Introduce multiplication practically using repeated addition or equal sets array within 25: use and interpret symbols.	66, 67, 68	55, 56, 57
N2.28	Investigate amounts of money using the least number of coins.	65	54
N2.29	Explore subtraction using a variety of practical apparatus e.g. abacus, base 10, games, calculator; present results orally and in written form.		
N2.30	Introduce the concept of fractions using whole shapes and sets of objects: (i) halves; (ii) quarters.	40, 41, 42, 43, 44	27, 28, 29, 30, 31, 32, 33, 34
N2.31	Approximate numbers up to 100, to the nearest 10.	37, 38, 39	24, 25, 26
N2.32	Apply knowledge of money to situations requiring addition and subtraction to £1.	63	52
N2.33	Develop vertical subtraction within 100 through formal recording: estimate answers to the nearest 10 before calculating.		
R2.1	Understand the use of a symbol to represent an answer	46, 54	36, 44
R2.2	Investigate odd and even numbers using practical materials.	22, 26	7, 11
R2.3	Explore and use patterns in addition and subtraction facts to 20.	45	35
R2.4	Count orally from a given number forwards and backwards in ones, twos, fives and tens: to 20; to 50; beyond	19, 20, 22, 25, 26, 27	3, 4, 6, 10, 11, 12
R2.5	Recognise odd and even numbers.	22, 28, 29	7, 13, 14
R2.6	Understand the use of a symbol to stand for an unknown number: 5 + * = 9	46, 54	36, 44
R2.7	Use extended addition to predict subsequent numbers	23, 24, 28	8, 9, 13
S2.1	Sort 3-D shapes giving reasons, e.g. roll, slide, stack	89	79
S2.2	Sort 2-D shapes giving reasons, e.g. three sides, fours corners.	88	78
S2.3	Name 2-D shapes – square, rectangle, triangle, circle.	88, 94	78, 84, 85
Sp2.1	Recognise turning movements, e.g. left, right, half turn, full turn.	92	82
Sp2.2	Follow instructions involving movements and turning.	92	83
Sp2.3	Use a computer controlled device e.g. Roamer to consolidate movement.		

Counting and writing numbers

Activity Sheet 1

Vocabulary

zero, one, two three...
one hundred, count on
from... to, count back
from... to, continue,
between

❏ Say the number names in order to at least 100, from and back to 0.

❏ Write whole numbers to at least 100 in figures.

❏ Describe and extend simple number sequences: count on or back in 1s, starting from any 2-digit number.

Resources
0–100 number cards (per pair)
0–100 number line (per pair)
2 counters

Misconceptions

Although the main focus of this activity is for children to develop their counting skills, it may be appropriate to discuss the use of the word 'between'. Sooner or later children will need to be aware that 'between' usually excludes the boundary numbers.

The key idea is that children tend to have more experience of counting from 1 or 0, but counting between two given numbers is a more sophisticated skill, developing a deeper understanding of the number system.

Children should have a sound knowledge of oral counting up to 100 and back, starting and ending at numbers other than 1 or 0, e.g. starting at 23 and counting on to 41, or counting back from 56 to 44. They will also need to be able to read 2-digit numbers or be able to find out what a number is from a visual aid in the classroom, e.g. a 100-square or number line.

❏ Encourage children to use or visualise the number line to help them.

❏ It is difficult to retain the end number while concentrating on counting, so it may help children remember when to stop if they keep both number cards in front of them and tap the space between the two cards until they reach the stop number.

❏ When children have played the game, suggest they change the rule to, e.g. saying the numbers backwards, or forwards and backwards.

❏ *Can you count without using the number line to help you?*

❏ *Can you just count the odd/even numbers?*

❏ *Have you changed the rules to your game?*

Answers
1 **a** 42, 43, 44, 45; **b** 60, 59, 58, 57; **c** 67, 68, 69, 70; **d** 51, 50, 49, 48;
e 13, 14, 15, 16; **f** 92, 91, 90, 89

Counting objects

Activity Sheet 2

Vocabulary

zero, one, two, three...
one hundred, count in
tens, units, ones,
exact, continue

❏ Count reliably up to 100 objects by grouping them in 10s.

Resources
a variety of objects to count, e.g. cubes, buttons, shells, straws (per child)
containers (per child)
sticky labels or Post-it notes (per child)

Teaching support

Misconceptions

Some children may count inaccurately. Encourage them to check each group after they have counted. They may benefit from using cubes, for example, so they can check that each of the groups of 10 is the same. They may get muddled, and need support to keep their work organised by having a place to put the objects they have already counted, and perhaps also labelling them.

The key idea is that there is a significant difference between oral counting and being able to count objects accurately. The main purpose of this activity is for children to learn how to count large numbers of objects efficiently. Children should begin to realise that, for numbers greater than 10, counting in 1s is less accurate than grouping.

Children should have a sound knowledge of oral counting and counting objects up to 100. They will need to be able to count in 10s, and begin to partition a number into 10s and 1s. They will also need to be able to read and write 2-digit numbers, and be able to find out what a number is from a visual aid in the classroom, e.g. a 100-square or number line.

- In question 2, encourage children to be systematic as they work, by using containers to hold their groups of 10. Some children may find it helpful to label each group "10", once it is complete.
- Help them understand that they need not count to any number greater than 10. Beyond that, they are counting groups of 10, and 1s.
- They may benefit from 'taking stock' and counting how many they have so far, after they have completed each group of 10.

Things to say and ask

- *Can you say how many tens and ones there will be before you count?*
- *How many more do you need?*
- *Now that you have finished this number, can you change your groups to show a different number without putting them all away and starting again?*
- *Say the number names in order to at least 100, from and back to 0.*

Answers

1 a 50 crayons   **b** 37 pens   **c** 44 balls   **d** 22 buns
    e 38 potatoes   **f** 63 carrots

Counting in 10s

Activity Sheet 3

Objectives

- Write whole numbers in figures to at least 100.
- Describe and extend simple number sequences: count on or back in 10s.

Vocabulary

zero, ten, twenty… one hundred, multiple of, in order

Resources

3 sets of multiples of 10 cards from 10 to 100 (per pair)
0–100 number line (per pair)

Teaching support

Misconceptions

Children are most likely to miss out numbers because they have not organised their cards in the most helpful way, rather than because they cannot recite the numbers. Encourage them to lay out their cards in order so it is easier to see what is missing.

The key idea is that the ability to count fluently supports many mental calculation strategies – it is also important in understanding place value, counting with money, estimating and approximating, and reading and interpreting scales. For all these activities, it is essential that children can recite the multiples of 10 on and back, and have a clear vision of how the multiples relate to each other on a number line.

Children should have a sound knowledge of oral counting in 10s, and grouping in 10s. It will also support their understanding if they have used a 0–100 number line to find all the multiples of 10.

- Children may need support in getting started with the game. If appropriate, suggest that they use a number line to help them identify where the numbers are in relation to each other, or get them to write out the multiples of 10 before they start, so they know what they are looking for.

Things to say and ask

❑ *Which numbers are missing from your collection?*
❑ *Can you play again, but this time collect the cards in order (reverse order)?*
❑ *Read the numbers that you have already.*

Answers

1 a 30, 40, 60, 70, 80, 90   b 0, 10, 20, 50, 60, 80, 90,100
   c 0, 10, 20, 30, 40, 70, 80, 100   d 20, 30, 40, 50, 60, 70, 90
   e 0, 20, 40, 50, 70, 80, 90, 100

Counting on in 10s

Activity Sheet 4

Objective

❑ Extend simple number sequences: count on or back in 1s or 10s from any 2-digit number.

Vocabulary

zero, ten, twenty …
one hundred, ten more,
ten less

Resources

1–100 number square (per pair)

Teaching support

The key idea is that there are two aspects to counting on in 10s. The first is the rhythm of the counting, i.e. that counting on 10 gets you to another number that ends in the same units digit: twenty-**three**, thirty-**three**, forty-**three** etc. The second aspect is that children need to be able to visualise the number growing with each extra ten. The ability to count on in 10s also supports many mental calculation strategies.

Misconceptions

Some children may count incorrectly by starting their count with the number they should count on from. For example, if they count on ten from 23 they may count: **23**, 24, 25, 26, 27, 28, 29, 30, 31, 32. By starting with 23, they are not counting on from 23; they should begin **24**, 25….

Children should have a sound knowledge of oral counting to 100 and back, starting and ending at numbers other than 1 or 0, e.g. starting at 23 and counting on to 41, or counting back from 56 to 44. They will also need to be able to count on and back between 0 and 100 in 10s.

◻ In question 1, encourage children to predict which number their next jump will take them to, and then check by counting if they need to.

◻ For the game, some children may find it helpful to use a 100-square to follow the sequence when they are listening to their partner counting back from one of the penguin numbers.

Things to say and ask

❑ *Can you count without using the number line or 100-square to help you?*
❑ *Which numbers are the easiest to count on or back from?*

Answers

1 a 34, 44, 54, 64   b 23, 33, 43, 53
   c 16, 26, 36, 46   d 40, 50, 60, 70
   e 4, 14, 24, 34   f 19, 29, 39, 49
   g 61, 71, 81, 91   h 54, 64, 74, 84

Counting on and back in 100s

Activity Sheet 5

Vocabulary

one hundred, two hundred... one thousand, continue, sequence

❏ Describe and extend simple number sequences: count in 100s from and back to 0.

Resources
scissors
glue

Misconceptions
Children are usually quick at being able to count on in 100s. The most common error is to say: ...eight hundred, nine hundred, ten hundred. Draw a parallel with counting in 10s, where the number after 'ninety' is not 'tenty'.

The key idea is that the ability to count in 10s and 100s supports many other number skills – mental calculation, place value, counting with money, estimating and approximating, reading and interpreting scales. For all of these it is essential that, in addition to reciting the multiples of 10 and 100 forwards and backwards, children have a clear image of where the multiples are in relation to each other on a number line.

Children should have a sound knowledge of oral counting on and back in 10s and 100s. They will also need to have talked about familiar numbers in 100s, e.g. the number of children in the school, a house number, the number of miles to a holiday destination.

❏ Make reference to work from place value sessions.

❏ A visual image may support the development of their understanding. For example, counting on in 100s while collecting 100-squares:

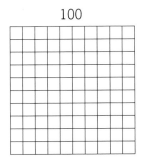 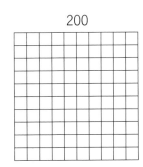 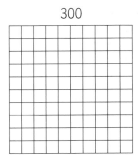

Or laying out a metre stick marked in centimetres while counting in 100s:

🔲 100 🔲 200 🔲 300 🔲 400 etc.

❏ *Which multiple of 100 is between 400 and 600?*
❏ *Which multiple of 100 is before 500?*
❏ *Can you say the numbers in reverse order without looking at your number line?*

Answers
1   **a**   5, 6, 7, 8, 9, 10   **b**   50, 60, 70, 80, 90
   c   500, 600, 700, 800, 900   **d**   7, 6, 5, 4, 3, 2, 1
   e   70, 60, 50, 40, 30, 20, 10   **f**   700, 600, 500, 400, 300, 200

Counting on and back in 2s

Activity Sheet 6

Objective

Vocabulary

rule, count in twos, every other, continue, between

❏ Describe and extend simple number sequences: count on in 2s from and back to 0 or any small number.

Resources

set of 15–30 number cards (per pair)

0–50 number line (per pair)

Teaching support

Misconceptions

Some children may find it more challenging to count the odd numbers than the even numbers. There may also be some children who can count in 2s starting from 1 or 2, but find it difficult to count from other numbers, or to count back.

The key idea is that children's attention needs to be drawn, even at this stage, to the units digit when counting in 2s. This is the first step towards recognising the general properties of odd and even numbers.

Children should have a sound knowledge of oral counting to 100 and back, starting and ending at numbers other than 1 or 0. They should also be able to count in 2s orally, or have practised counting every other number loudly, then quietly.

❏ Encourage children to focus on the 'every other number' rule, for counting in 2s, and to use a 0–50 number line for support.

❏ If necessary, encourage children to circle every other number on the number line, so they can see what comes next.

❏ For the game, children should start with the pile of cards face down. Allow them to look at a marked number line for their first few turns.

Things to say and ask

❏ *Can you count without using the number line to help you?*
❏ *If you count in twos from two, and in twos from one, do you say the same numbers?*
❏ *What numbers would you say if you carried on past fifty?*

Answers

1 a 10, 12, 14   **b** 7, 11, 13   **c** 11, 13, 17   **d** 14, 12, 10

2 11, 51; 4, 50; 13, 51; 16, 50; 15, 51; 19, 51; 8, 50; 6, 50

Odd and even numbers

Activity Sheet 7

Objectives

Vocabulary

odd, even, every other, multiple of, sequence, predict

❏ Recognise odd and even numbers to at least 30.
❏ Begin to recognise 2-digit multiples of two.

Resources

30 interlocking cubes (per child)

The key idea is to help children recognise the general properties of odd and even numbers.

There are two useful visual images for odd and even-ness. The first, raised in the Activity Sheet, is when children split a quantity into two equal parts to ascertain its even-ness. The other image, not practised in this Activity Sheet, is sorting items into pairs. An even number being defined, in this instance, as a quantity that sorts into pairs with no leftovers!

Children should have a sound knowledge of oral and written counting to 30 and back in 1s and 2s.

■ In question 1, children should predict the outcome for each number before they try it with cubes. Ask them to explain their predictions, and help them to differentiate between hunches and reasoned predictions. They will need support in using the language of odd and even numbers.

Teaching support

Misconceptions

A common error in question 1 is miscounting. Encourage children to check their work by counting the total number of cubes after they have made the two towers, as well as before. Suggest they count in 2s:

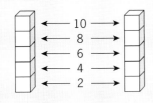

Things to say and ask

❏ *Can you predict which numbers will be odd, and which will be even?*
❏ *Look at the units digits of the even numbers on your number line. What do you notice?*

Answers

1 b 4, 8, 14, 12, 6, 18, 26

c

1	2	3	4	5	6	7	8	9	10	11	12	13	14	15	16	17	18	19	20	21	22	23	24	25	26	27	28	29	30
	✓		✓		✓		✓		✓		✓		✓		✓		✓		✓		✓		✓		✓		✓		✓

Counting in 3s

Activity Sheet 8

Objective

❏ Describe and extend simple number sequences: count on in steps of three to at least 30, from and back to 0, then from and back to any given small number.

Vocabulary

count in threes, multiple of, sequence, continue

Resources

2 cm squared paper (per child)
0–30 number line (per child)

Teaching support

Misconceptions

The most common error is miscounting. One error throws out the rest of the pattern. Encourage children to check the pattern backwards. This focuses them on the "one, two, three" pattern and they usually identify their own errors.

The key idea is to reinforce a pattern of numbers in two visual ways. First, on a number line, where the pattern of 3s can be seen in the two spaces between each of the chosen numbers. Secondly, in the number squares, where a repeating pattern emerges in different forms in different sizes of square. Some children may be able to see the connection between the size of the square and the type of pattern. (If the number of columns is a multiple of 3, the pattern will have vertical lines.)

Children should have a sound knowledge of oral counting to 50 and back in 1s and in 2s, and be able to identify or follow these numbers on a class number line. They should also have used number squares in other contexts.

■ In question 1, encourage children to predict and check each number on the number lines. Show them that the number lines begin with a number with a 1 in the units place. Can they find the places where the lines overlap? Can they use the previous line to help them?

❏ Explain that once they have finished finding the patterns in the number squares in question 2, they can draw any sized square themselves on 2cm squared paper and try the same thing. Children may need support in drawing a square with appropriate dimensions!

❏ For question 3, ask children what patterns they have found.

❏ Use the number line to practise counting on and back in steps of 3 from zero. If time permits, also try counting on from and back to any small number.

❏ *Which number do you think will be next in the sequence?*
❏ *What do you think will be the last multiple of 3 in the square?*
❏ *Can you say the multiples of 3 starting at 3 without looking at your sheet?*

Answers

1 a

1	2	3 ✗	4	5	6	7	8	9	10	11	12	13	14	15	16

b

11	12 ✗	13	14	15	16	17	18	19	20	21	22	23	24	25	26

c

21 ✗	22	23	24	25	26	27	28	29	30	31	32	33	34	35	36

d

31	32	33 ✗	34	35	36	37	38	39	40	41	42	43	44	45	46

e

41	42 ✗	43	44	45	46	47	48	49	50	51	52	53	54	55	56

2 a

1	2	3
4	5	6
7	8	9

b

1	2	3	4
5	6	7	8
9	10	11	12
13	14	15	16

c

1	2	3	4	5	6
7	8	9	10	11	12
13	14	15	16	17	18
19	20	21	22	23	24
25	26	27	28	29	30
31	32	33	34	35	36

d

1	2	3	4	5	6	7
8	9	10	11	12	13	14
15	16	17	18	19	20	21
22	23	24	25	26	27	28
29	30	31	32	33	34	35
36	37	38	39	40	41	42
43	44	45	46	47	48	49

3 Number square patterns a and c are similar and patterns b and d are similar.

Counting in 4s

Activity Sheet 9

Vocabulary

count in fours, multiple of, sequence, continue

❏ Describe and extend simple number sequences: count on in steps of four to at least 30, from and back to 0, then from and back to any given small number.

Resources

0–50 number line (per child)

calculator (per pair)

counter (per child)

1–100 number square

Teaching support

Misconceptions

Some children may incorrectly start their count with the number they should be counting on from. For example, to count on 4 from 5 they may say **5**, 6, 7, 8, when they should say **6**, 7, 8, 9.

The key idea is to reinforce number patterns in different ways. First as a sequence, where the start and end numbers are different, and the sequences run on and back. Secondly on a 1–100 number square, and thirdly using the constant function on a calculator. The calculator establishes the connection between the sequence of 4s and the repeated addition of 4.

Children should have a sound knowledge of oral counting to 50 and back, in 1s, 2s and 3s, and be able to identify or follow these numbers on a class number line. They should also have used a calculator and number squares in other contexts.

- In question 1, some children may want the support of a number line for the sequencing activity. They may find it helpful to identify the sequence of 4s on the number line, and then establish the range of numbers they are focusing on. This will help them to identify what is missing.

- In the game, the calculator can be used to generate the sequence of 4s in two ways. Firstly by using the constant function (4+===, or 4 +++ on most calculators), and secondly by repeatedly adding 4 (i.e. 4 + =, +=, += etc)

- To make the game harder, suggest children start counting from numbers other than 4. (Use the constant function on the calculator to count on from 5, for example, by keying 5 + 4 === ......)

Things to say and ask

- *How do you know which number is next?*
- *What do you think will be the last multiple of four on the number square?*
- *Can you say the multiples of four starting at four without looking at the number line or the number square?*

Answers

1	a	12	b	16	c	20	d	25

Counting in 5s and 10s

Activity Sheet 10

Objectives

- Begin to recognise 2-digit multiples of 5 and 10.
- Investigate a general statement about familiar numbers by finding examples that satisfy it.

Vocabulary

count in ..., multiple of, number grid

Resources
none

Teaching support

Misconceptions

Some children may find it difficult to make the connection between identifying the multiples of 5 and 10 and responding to the questions. Encourage them to study the patterns that the multiples have made without reading the statements.

The key idea is to highlight properties of multiples of 5 and 10. (Multiples of 10 all end in 0 and are even, multiples of 5 end in 0 or 5 and alternate even/odd.) Deciding whether or not a general statement is true supports the development of children's reasoning, and their ability to check their own work.

Children should have a sound knowledge of oral counting to 50 and back, counting in 5s and 10s, and should be able to identify or follow these numbers on a class number line or 100-square. They should also have some experience of making observations, not necessarily in mathematics (in science, perhaps), and of drawing some conclusions.

- If this is the first time children have seen true/false statements, they may need support to get started.

- They could work in pairs, to encourage them to discuss and justify their ideas.

- Encourage children to read the statements out loud.

❑ *Will 50 have a smile?*
❑ *What do you think will be the next number with a tick and a smile?*
❑ *Do you think 100 will have a tick, a smile, or both?*

Answers

1	a 20	b 20	c 10	d 15
	e 0	f 15	g 5	h 25
	i 15	j 10	k 20	l 15
	m 5	n 30	o 20	

2

0 ✓ ☺	1	2	3	4	5 ✓	6	7	8	9
10 ✓ ☺	11	12	13	14	15 ✓	16	17	18	19
20 ✓ ☺	21	22	23	24	25 ✓	26	27	28	29
30 ✓ ☺	31	32	33	34	35 ✓	36	37	38	39
40 ✓ ☺	41	42	43	44	45 ✓	46	47	48	49

3 a   35 is in the pattern of 5s ✓
    b   All the numbers in the pattern of 5s are even ✕
    c   All the numbers in the pattern of 5s end in 5 ✕
    d   All the numbers in the pattern of 10s end in 0 ✓

Counting in 2s

Activity Sheet 11

Vocabulary

count on from…to,
count back from… to,
count in, multiple of,
continue

❑ Begin to recognise 2-digit multiples of 2.
❑ Investigate a general statement about familiar numbers by finding examples that satisfy it.

Resources
0–50 number line (per child)
twenty 2p coins (per pair)

Misconceptions

The main focus of the game is to recognise multiples of 2 by identifying the units digit. Some children may be thrown by the context of money, and will need to concentrate on the actual amounts. These children could undertake a similar counting activity on another occasion using interlocking cubes joined in pairs (like the ones below) instead of coins.

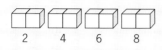

2   4   6   8

Things to say and ask

The key idea is to draw children's attention to the general properties of multiples of 2, i.e. that they all end in an even digit. They also look at the pattern of the multiples of 2 in the context of money.

Children should have a sound knowledge of oral counting to 50 in 1s and 2s, starting and ending at numbers other than 1 or 0. They will need some experience of handling money, knowing the value of a 2p coin, for example. They will also need to be able to write 2-digit numbers up to 50, or be able to find out how to write a number from a visual aid in the classroom, such as a 100-square or number line.

❏ Children may need support in getting started on their list of amounts. When their list is 'complete' and they have put all twenty 2p coins in the purse and recorded the amounts, draw their attention to the amounts of money, and elicit from them that this is the sequence of 2s… or the even numbers.

❏ Direct children to the units digit of each number, and confirm with them that these numbers always end with 0, 2, 4, 6 or 8.

❏ *Could you make 21p using only 2p coins?*
❏ *Are the amounts you have made odd numbers or even numbers?*
❏ *What digit(s) do multiples of 2 always end in?*

Answers

1	**a** 4→6	**b** 10→12	**c** 20→22	**d** 2→4	**e** 6→8	**f** 8→10
	g 22→24	**h** 12→14	**i** 10→12	**j** 18→20	**k** 24→26	**l** 30→32.

Continuing patterns

Activity Sheet 12

Objectives

Vocabulary

pattern, puzzle, sequence, continue, predict, multiple of

❏ Solve mathematical problems or puzzles, recognise simple patterns and relationships, generalise and predict.

❏ Describe and extend simple number sequences: count on in steps of 2, 3, 4, 5 or 10 to at least 30, from and back to 0.

Resources

large 1–100 number square (per group)
up to 50 small counters in 5 different colours (per pair)

Teaching support

Misconceptions

In the game, some children may focus on the numbers rather than the pattern. Direct them to the pattern of 5s or 10s to begin with. Draw their attention to the straight lines generated by the counters, and ask them to predict where the next counters will go.

The key idea in the game is that children should observe and continue the physical pattern generated on the square (rather than the number sequence itself) based on their previous experience of patterns generated by number sequences.

Children should have a sound knowledge of oral counting to 50 in 1s, 2s, 3s, 4s, 5s and 10s.

❏ Understanding the objective of the game will be clarified if, as an introduction to the activity, children discuss the patterns generated by different sequences on a large 100-square.

Things to say and ask

❏ *What number do you think would go there (pointing at a square with a counter but no number)?*
❏ *Which numbers make straight lines?*
❏ *Are there any patterns that are similar?*

Answers

1 **a** 7, 9, 11, 13   **b** 17, 19, 21, 23
   c 35, 45, 55, 65   **d** 14, 18, 22, 26

Number rules

Activity Sheet 13

Objectives

Vocabulary

describe the pattern,
describe the rule,
sequence, multiple of

❏ Investigate a general statement about familiar numbers by finding examples that satisfy it.
❏ Recognise odd and even numbers to at least 30.
❏ Describe and extend simple number sequences: count on in steps of 2, 3, 4, 5 or 10 to at least 30.

Resources
1–50 number cards (per pair)

Teaching support

Misconceptions
Many possible misconceptions are addressed by the paired work in the game. Most commonly, children will be unsure about a particular property of one of the patterns. They may benefit from revisiting a previous activity where they learned about that particular aspect of number properties.

The key idea is that children should respond to a general statement, and use what they know about the properties described to identify some numbers that fit the statement. The activities expect children to draw on what they know about sequencing and patterns in numbers.

Children should have a sound knowledge of extending and describing number sequences, particularly multiples of 2, 3, 4, 5 and 10. They should also be familiar with odd and even numbers and their properties, and be able to recognise and read numbers up to 50.

▢ Question 1 and the game are open activities where children use and apply what they know. They will benefit from some oral preparation; say, for example, *Think of an odd number*, or, *Think of a number in the pattern of 10s*.

▢ They will also benefit from a few reminders about how to recognise certain numbers:
  – Even numbers end in 0, 2, 4, 6 or 8
  – Multiples of 10 always end in 0
  – Numbers in the pattern of 5s end in 5 or 0
  – Odd numbers end in 1, 3, 5, 7 or 9
  – Multiples of 4 are even.

Things to say and ask

❏ *How do you know that 21 is an odd number?*
❏ *Do you know a number that is in the pattern of threes and the pattern of tens?*
❏ *What is the smallest odd number you know? What is the biggest?*

Answers

(Children will be identifying their own numbers.)

Explaining odd and even numbers

Activity Sheet 14

Objectives

❑ Explain how a problem was solved orally and, where appropriate, in writing.
❑ Recognise odd and even numbers to at least 30.

Vocabulary

odd, even, sum, explain your method

Resources

counters (to use instead of marbles)

Teaching support

Misconceptions

It is unlikely that errors will centre on the mathematics. Most errors will occur when children have not understood the question properly. Encourage them to read the question out loud, or ask a friend to read it to them. Clarify what they are asked to find out, and let them try one or two examples in your presence.

The key idea is that children should use their knowledge of odd and even numbers to solve problems. In question 3 they could use trial and improvement, or the strategy of sorting the 'marbles' into three equal piles and transferring two 'marbles' from Dong's pile to Pip's pile. They should record their thinking in pictures or in words.

Children should be confident in recognising and using odd and even numbers, and be able to add three numbers together. They should also have experience of explaining their thinking out loud.

▪ Children may have difficulty putting their explanations on paper. Encourage them to explain their method orally first, then record each step in pictures or words.

▪ Allow sufficient time for children to explain their strategies, either individually or as part of the plenary. If the children work in pairs, they will have an extra opportunity to explain their thinking to a peer.

▪ Children may like to use their recordings as a prop when explaining their reasoning.

Things to say and ask

❑ *How will you start?*
❑ *What do we know so far?*
❑ *What could we try next?*
❑ *How did you work it out?*

Answers

1 and 2 Child's own answers.
3 Pip 9, Bing 7, Dong 5

Reading and writing numbers

Activity Sheet 15

Objective

❑ Read and write whole numbers to at least 100 in figures and words.

Vocabulary

numbers, digit, figure, write in figures, tens, units, ones

Resources

number cards for the multiples of 10 from 0–100 (per group)
1–100 number square (per group)
spellings of multiples of 10 to 100 (per group)
0–9 digit cards (per child)

Teaching support

Misconceptions

Children often transpose the digits in 'teens' numbers so 'seventeen' is written in the order in which it is said, i.e. 71. By comparison, the numbers from 20 to 100 are written in the order they are spoken, e.g. seventy-three is 73.

The key idea is to give children practice in recognising numbers to one hundred written in words. In question 2 they choose pairs of digit cards to create 2-digit numbers, and write the numbers in words. In question 3 the link between figures and words is made in the context of prices of animals.

Children should have a sound knowledge of numbers to twenty and should appreciate the patterns within numbers up to one hundred, e.g. ...ty-one, ...ty-two, ...ty-three etc. They should be able to write the numbers one to nine in words.

◻ Revise multiples of 10 up to 100 by showing number cards, e.g. 60, 20, 70. Invite the children to write these numbers in words. Practise counting on in 1s from these numbers, e.g. 21, 22, 23, 24...

◻ Use a 1–100 number square to remind children of the patterns of digits. Emphasise the ...ty-one, ...ty-two, ...ty-three... pattern and discuss the multiples of 10 that follow ....ty-nine.

◻ Some children might benefit from a list of spellings of the multiples of 10.

Things to say and ask

◻ *Which is the largest number on the sheet?*
◻ *How would you say it?*
◻ *If we changed the order of the digit cards, what would each number be then?*

Answers

| **1** | **a** 17 | **b** 23 | **c** 32 | **d** 48 | **e** 71 | **f** 84 |

2 and **3** Child's own answers.

Understanding digits

Activity Sheet 16

Objective

◻ Know what each digit in a 2-digit number represents, including 0 as a place holder.

Vocabulary

tens, units, ones, digit, 2-digit number, stands for, represents, nearest

Resources

place value cards (per group)

0–100 number line (per child)

0–9 digit cards (per pair)

20 counters (per pair)

Teaching support

Misconceptions

Children often transpose the digits in 'teens' numbers, so 'seventeen' is written in the order in which it is said, i.e. 71. When children don't understand the relative value of the digits, they may, for example, write 'sixty-three' as 603.

The key idea is that children should recognise numbers as made up of tens and units. In question 2, it may be useful for children to have a 0–100 number line to check their answers.

Children should already understand that the 'teens numbers' can be broken into '10 and ...', e.g. that 14 is 10 and 4 1s (units). This should lead to a realisation that the 1 stands for 1 ten, and if a 2-digit number begins with a 2, it stands for 2 tens etc. They should also be confident with the idea that 2 tens is the same as 20, 3 tens is the same as 30, etc.

◻ Revise tens and units (ones) using place value cards. Make several 2-digit numbers and ask the children to say how many tens and how many units each has. Stress the link between the number of tens and the multiple of 10, e.g. that 3 tens is the same as 30. Identify these numbers on a 0–100 number line and compare them.

◻ Refer children to question 2 and explain the task to them. Go through a few examples with them ensuring they understand the meaning of the word 'nearest'.

Things to say and ask

- ❏ *Why do you think that number is nearest to sixty? How far from sixty is that number?*
- ❏ *Could you make a different number that is only two away?*
- ❏ *How many tens/units make up the number?*
- ❏ *What does the two stand for in this number?*
- ❏ *What is the largest number you can make with two of these digits?*

Answers

1
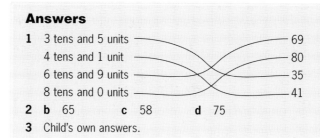

2   **b** 65   **c** 58   **d** 75

3   Child's own answers.

Splitting numbers into tens and units

Activity Sheet 17

Objectives

Vocabulary

tens, units, ones, digit, 2-digit, number, place value, split, stands for, represents

- ❏ Know what each digit in a 2-digit number represents, and partition 2-digit numbers into a multiple of ten and ones (TU).
- ❏ Use the = sign to represent equality.

Resources
set of place value cards (per group and per pair)

Teaching support

Misconceptions

Children may be unsure of how to partition numbers that are multiples of 10, e.g. 90. Encourage them to see that there are 9 tens and 0 units.

The key idea is that children should partition (split) 2-digit numbers into tens and units and recombine them. These skills are vital in coming to understand place value.

Children should be familiar with place value cards and how to arrange them on top of each other. They should be confident with the terms 'tens' and 'units' (or ones), and have some experience of partitioning 'teens' numbers into 10 + …. They should also have had experience of ordering numbers.

- ◗ Revise partitioning 'teens' numbers into 10 + …. units using place value cards.
- ◗ Make a 2-digit number between 20 and 29 and ask children to say how many tens and how many units it has. Show that the first 2 represents 20 or 2 tens. Remind children that the first digit shows how many tens the number has and the second digit shows how many units or ones it has. Make use of the = sign.

Things to say and ask

- ❏ *Point to a number with eight in the tens column, one in the units column etc.*
- ❏ *How do you know that's the smallest number?*
- ❏ *Why is that the next smallest?*
- ❏ *How many numbers between thirty and sixty have the digit five in them? What does the five stand for in thirty-five, forty-five, fifty, fifty-one… etc.?*

Answers

1   **b** 43 = 4 tens and 3 units   **c** 81 = 8 tens and 1 unit   **d** 90 = 9 tens and 0 units

2   23, 24, 28, 73, 74, 78

Comparing and ordering

Activity Sheet 18

Objective

Vocabulary

twenty-first, twenty-second …last, between, next to, larger, smaller, more, less

❑ Use and begin to read the vocabulary of comparing and ordering numbers, including ordinal numbers to 100.

Resources

10 or more coloured cubes or objects (per group)

0–100 number cards (per pair)

0–100 number lines (per child)

Teaching support

Misconceptions

In question 2, pairs of numbers are transposed as in 16 and 61 to highlight any children who are not yet using place value effectively to judge the relative sizes of numbers. Provide children with 0–100 number lines if necessary.

The key idea is that children should be able to use ordinal numbers, e.g. twentieth, fifteenth, and to compare and order numbers to 100.

Children should be confident with ordinal numbers to at least 20. To revise this, show children a set of 10 or more coloured cubes or objects in a line. Ask *Which is the ninth item? Can you point to it? What colour is the third item?* etc. You could also ask children to say the date of their birthday.

◼ When children are working out, e.g., the twenty-first letter in the alphabet they may find it easier to count using cardinal numbers one, two, three… to twenty-one, rather than first, second, third, fourth… Demonstrate both ways and let them use the way they find easier. Point out that once they have worked out one answer, e.g. the twenty-first, it can be used to help them find another, e.g. the twenty-fourth, by counting on, rather than starting again at the first.

◼ For question 3, children could be given a smaller range of number cards.

◼ If necessary, play the game once with children to demonstrate the rules.

Things to say and ask

❑ For question 1: *What letter is in the eleventh star? What position is the letter g?*
❑ *Why is 65 larger than 56? How can you tell?*
❑ *Can you tell me a number that lies in between 56 and 65?*
❑ *I'm thinking of a number between 38 and 43. What could it be?*

Answers

1   u, x, r

2   **a** 56   **b** 37   **c** 16
    d 38   **e** 40   **f** 89

Comparing numbers

Activity Sheet 19

Objective

Vocabulary

larger, smaller, more, less, tens, units, place value, compare

❏ Compare 2 given 2-digit numbers, say which is more or less, and give a number that lies between them.

Resources
0–100 number line (per group)
red and yellow pencil or crayon (per child)

Teaching support

Misconceptions
Children who do not fully understand place value sometimes add the digits to make a guess at which is larger or smaller, e.g. 79 might seem larger than 81 as 7 and 9 have a greater total than 8 and 1. Revise tens and units and focus their attention on the value of the tens digit as a means of comparing.

The key idea is that children should compare numbers, saying which is larger or smaller. Initially, they identify numbers above and below 50. Next they create pairs of 2-digit numbers from 4 given digits, and compare the numbers to each other. Finally, they are asked to give a number that lies in between each pair.

Children should know that 2-digit numbers are made from a tens digit and a units digit. They should already have experience of comparing numbers to at least 20.

▪ Use a 0–100 number line and call out pairs of 2-digit numbers. Invite children to find them on the number line and to say which is larger or smaller. They should then give a number that lies between the two. Encourage them to describe how they can tell whether a specific 2-digit number is larger than another, e.g. by looking at the tens digit first.

Things to say and ask

❏ For question 1: *What word is coloured yellow?*
❏ *Can you give me some other numbers that are more/less than 50?*
❏ *Give me a number that is more than 20 but less than 30.*
❏ *A number lies between 47 and 53. What could it be?*
❏ *This ball cost between 50p and 70p. What could it have cost? What else might it have cost? What couldn't it have cost?*

Answers
1 If all correct, 'Hi' should be coloured in yellow.

23	67	33	91	15
42	72	17	63	55
14	49	30	52	47
9	51	28	80	32
39	69	16	98	40

2 and 3 Child's own answers.

1 or 10 more or less

Activity Sheet 20

Objective

❏ Say the number that is 1 or 10 more or less than any given 2-digit number.

Vocabulary

one, ten, more, less, pattern, digit, tens, units, ones

Resources

1–100 number square (per group)

0–100 number line (per group)

5 different colouring pencils (per child)

Teaching support

Misconceptions

Some children take time to understand the relative positions of the multiples of 10. For example, when counting back they may think that the number between 41 and 39 is 30. Usually they have learned an incorrect pattern through saying the numbers aloud, e.g. forty-two, forty-one, **thirty**, thirty-nine, thirty-eight … Use a number line, and encourage children to look at the place value of the digits, e.g. thirty is 3 tens and no units.

The key idea is that children should identify numbers that are 1 or 10 more or less than any given 2-digit numbers. This includes numbers that cross the 10s boundary, e.g. 1 less than 70.

Children should have experience in adding or subtracting 1 or 10 to or from numbers up to 30. They should appreciate patterns within numbers, e.g. 10 more than 4 is 14, and 10 more than 14 is 24, etc.

■ Encourage children to recognise that, when adding or subtracting 10, the units digit is unchanged, e.g. 10 more than 46 is 56. Some children may begin by counting on in 1s when adding 10, rather than just adding 1 to the tens digit. Use a 1–100 number square to highlight these ideas by counting up or down in 10s from any number on the square.

■ Give oral practice by asking questions such as: *What is 1 more than 47? Than 68? Than 102? What is 1 less than 59? Than 80? Than 110? What number is 10 more than 83? Less than 29? What number is 10 after 54? 10 before 105?*

Things to say and ask

❏ *What are we doing when we find a number that is 1 or 10 more?*

❏ *What are we doing when we find a number that is 1 or 10 less?*

❏ *What do you notice when you add or subtract 10?*

❏ *How can you save time when finding 10 more? Do we have to count on in ones?*

❏ *Let's put 50 at the end of the chain in question 3 and work backwards. What do you think the start number might be?*

Answers

1	a	38	b	46	c	80
2	a	54	b	70	c	79

3 51, 50, 60, 59, 49, 39, 40, 41, 51, 52, 42, 41, 40

(The final number in the chain should be the same as the start number.)

1 or 10 more or less puzzles

Activity Sheet 21

Objective

Vocabulary

one, ten, more, less, digit, tens, units, ones

❏ Say the number that is 1 or 10 more or less than any given 2-digit number.

Resources

'1 more', '1 less', '10 more' and '10 less' labels
10–50 number cards (per pair)

Teaching support

Misconceptions

Make it clear that the number chains in question 3 work from left to right.

In the game, ensure that children don't just focus on the units digits, and claim incorrectly that, e.g., 16 and 36 make a pair.

The key idea is that children solve puzzles by deciding what has happened to each successive number in the terms '1 more', '10 less' etc. The activities explore the idea that taking the step of finding 10 more can be 'undone' by then finding 10 less.

Children should already be confident with finding 1 or 10 more or less with numbers up to 30. They should recognise that, when adding or subtracting 10, the units digit is unchanged. This can help them to recognise when 1 or 10 has been added to or subtracted from a number. This activity could usefully follow Activity Sheet 20, as a further extension of the same ideas.

▪ As an introduction to question 3, it might be helpful to use labels with the headings 1 more, 1 less, 10 more, 10 less. Ask a child to choose a number between 20 and 80 as a start number. Show one of the labels, and let the child work out the new number. This activity can continue, forming a number chain. Encourage children to identify a start number if the second number in the chain was, say, 25. If the label was 10 more, the start number would be 10 less than 25, i.e. 15.

▪ If necessary, play the game to demonstrate the rules. Children are looking for pairs of cards with a difference of 10, e.g. 35 and 45. They start with 6 cards each and put the remaining cards in a pile face down between them. If they can make a pair of cards, such as 16 and 26, they put the pair on the table, face up. Then they take it in turns to expose the top card from the pack, taking it if they want to, and putting down a new pair if the exposed card helps them. The winner is the first child with four pairs.

Things to say and ask

❏ *What do you notice when you say the number ten more/less?*
❏ *What do you think this label might be? How can you check if you are right?*
❏ *What happens if you work backwards, from right to left?*
❏ *Can you make up your own chain using these labels that starts and finishes on the same number?*

Answers

1	**b** 61		**c** 79		**d** 100		**e** 53	
2	**a** 34		**b** 49		**c** 71		**d** 69	**e** 80

3	**a**	15	10 more	25	**1 less**	24	**10 more**	34
	b	39	**1 more**	40	**10 more**	50	**1 less**	49
	c	**36**	10 more	46	1 less	**45**	10 more	**55**

Ordering numbers

Activity Sheet 22

Objectives

Vocabulary

smaller, larger, order

❑ Order whole numbers to at least 100.

❑ Know what each digit in a 2-digit number represents, including 0 as a place holder.

Resources
0–100 number line or 1–100 number square (per child)

Teaching support

Misconceptions
As well as comparing 2-digit numbers to judge relative size, children need to have a sense of the size of the numbers as a whole.

The key idea is to highlight the strategy of being systematic when trying to find all possible numbers in question 2. Children can simplify the task by exploring all the possibilities for 6 in the units, and then find those with 6 in the tens place.

Children need to know the value of each digit in a 2-digit number, and to realise that the digit 6 can occupy either the tens or the units place.

◼ Call out 4 or 5 2-digit numbers or select pairs of digits to create numbers between 10 and 100. Taking each number in turn, invite children to find and mark it on a 0–100 number line. Ask questions as each new number is introduced, e.g. *Is this larger than the last number? How can you tell? Does this come between these two numbers? Which is the largest of all the numbers?* Encourage children to describe how they can tell whether one specific 2-digit number is larger than another.

Things to say and ask

❑ *Check that you don't repeat a number in your list.*
❑ *How can you be sure you have found all the numbers? What could you use to help you?*
❑ *How many of your numbers have a 6 as the units digit? As the tens digit?*
❑ *How many 2-digit numbers can you make that have a 9 in them? Can you put them in order?*
❑ *How do you know which is the smallest/largest?*

Answers
1 **a** 26, 35, 53, 87 **b** 69, 71, 78, 94
2 The 18 numbers are: 16, 26, 36, 46, 56, 66, 76, 86, 96, 60, 61, 62, 63, 64, 65, 67, 68, 69.
In order: 16, 26, 36, 46, 56, 60, 61, 62, 63, 64, 65, 66, 67, 68, 69, 76, 86, 96.
3 There are 20 possibilities: 12, 13, 17, 19, 21, 23, 27, 29, 31, 32, 37, 39, 71, 72, 73, 79, 91, 92, 93, 97.

Ordering and placing numbers

Activity Sheet 23

Objectives

Vocabulary

hundred square, tens, units, more than, less than, row, column, correct

❑ Order whole numbers to 100 and position them on a number line and 100-square.

❑ Know what each digit in a 2-digit number represents, including 0 as a place holder.

Resources
1–100 number square (per child)

Teaching support

The key idea is that the 100-square helps children to develop an awareness of how numbers relate to each other. If they are confident, they can attempt to fill in the missing numbers in question 3 without the 100-square.

- Practise counting on in 1s from any 2-digit number to remind children of the patterns within numbers to 100, e.g. ...ty-one, ...ty-two, ...ty-three etc.
- Revise the multiples of 10 to 100 and write them in order.
- Draw children's attention to the digits in the 10s column, e.g. **1**0, **2**0, **3**0, **4**0, **5**0, ... and encourage them to see that the 10s digits go up in 1s as the multiples of 10 are counted.
- Discuss patterns within rows and columns on a 100-square, e.g. show that each number in a column is 10 more or less than the number above or below.
- Give children a copy of a 100-square cut into several pieces. Ask them to put it together.

Things to say and ask

- ❏ *Which digit in this number is the same as one in this number, e.g. 38 and 48?*
- ❏ *Is it the tens digit that is the same or the units digit?*
- ❏ *How many more is 48 than 38?*
- ❏ *What do you notice about the way numbers in a row/column are arranged?*

Answers

1 36 38 40

2 10 20 30 40 50 60 70 80 90

3 **a** 49 **b** 39 40 50   **c** 61 71 72 73

4

								39	40
41	42		44						
	52	53	54					59	
			64	65	66	67	68		
	72	73	74	75	76	77	78		
	82		84			87	88		
			94			97	98		100

Estimating

Activity Sheet 24

Objectives

- ❏ Use and begin to read the vocabulary of estimation and approximation.
- ❏ Give a sensible estimate of at least 50 objects.

Vocabulary

guess how many, estimate, roughly, close to, nearly, about, exact, exactly

Resources
sets of up to 30 cubes, conkers, plastic animals, etc. (per child)
about 50 counters (per pair)

Misconceptions

Children often believe that an estimate is worthless unless it produces the actual number or very close to it. This can lead them to count first and then give an estimate by adjusting by 1 or 2 items. Encourage children to see that an estimate only provides a rough idea of the actual number.

The key idea is that an estimate is a 'good guess' that improves with experience. Here children are involved in estimating and then counting sets of drawn objects, items in the classroom, and counters as part of a game.

It is important for children to have as much practical experience of estimating real life objects as possible. This enables them to build up a much greater sense of the size of numbers. Provide sets of up to 30 cubes, conkers, plastic animals, etc. before children tackle these activities.

❑ Discuss grouping strategies, mentally grouping objects in 5s, for example, and then counting the sets of 5, to help children to give good estimates. Stress that it is not vital to calculate the exact number.

Things to say and ask

❑ *Why do you think there are forty? How did you decide on that estimate?*
❑ *If there are thirty in this set, how many do you think are in that set?*
❑ *How many do you think there are in half this set?*

Answers

1 a 27   **b** 30   **c** 50

Estimating and number lines

Activity Sheet 25

Objectives

Vocabulary

guess how many, estimate, roughly, close to, nearly, about

❑ Use and begin to read the vocabulary of estimation and approximation.

❑ Give a sensible estimate of at least 50 objects.

Resources
set of flashcards with the key vocabulary

Teaching support

Misconceptions

In questions 2 and 3, children need to realise the importance of looking at the numbers at both the left and right-hand extremes of each line in order to know how many numbers are represented along its length.

The key idea is that an estimate is a 'good guess' that improves with experience. Strategies that involve mentally grouping objects in 5s, for example, and then counting the sets of 5 will help children to give good estimates. Questions 2 and 3 provide opportunities for children to develop a sense of where numbers lie in relation to each other on number lines. Marks to show equal divisions have been put on the number lines in question 2 to encourage children to see how a line can be split, in order to help estimate the numbers.

The strategy of visualising the line being divided into equal parts is more difficult and requires a lot of practice.

❑ Discuss mental grouping strategies to help children to give good estimates. Stress that it is not vital to estimate the exact number.

❑ In question 1, children might find it useful to mark the items as they count them.

❑ Demonstrate how a number line can be divided into two equal parts, writing the 'halfway number' and then repeating the process to subdivide the line still further.

❑ Invite children to make up sentences using the flashcards.

Things to say and ask
- ❏ *Why do you think this number is fifteen? What did you do to work it out?*
- ❏ *What could we do that would be better than just guessing?*
- ❏ *If the whole line is twenty, what will the halfway number be?*
- ❏ *What number will come just before twenty? Just after ten?*

Answers

1	**a**	47	**b**	63				
2	**a**	5, 9	**b**	10, 18	**c**	50, 90		
3	**a**	5	**b**	3	**c**	10	**d**	50

Rounding numbers

Activity Sheet 26

Objective

Vocabulary

round, nearest, round to the nearest ten, exactly, about

❏ Round numbers less than 100 to the nearest 10.

Resources
0–100 number line (per child)
set of 0–9 digit cards (per pair)

Teaching support

Misconceptions

Children sometimes round a number by looking at the 10s digit only, so they might think that all numbers in the thirties will be rounded to 30. Use a number line or 100-square to explore this error.

The key idea is that rounding a number to the nearest 10 gives an approximate number that is often easier to work with. The children need to have a clear mental picture of where numbers lie in relation to each other on the number line. When rounding to the nearest 10, the answer will be a multiple of 10 (or 0).

- ■ Begin by counting on from 0 in 10s, e.g. 0, 10, 20, 30 … to 100 and back. Explain that these numbers will be important for today's activity.

- ■ Introduce the idea of rounding, using a real life context such as *You are walking along a street, and you know the people who live at numbers 10, 20, 30 and 40. It starts to rain. If you were outside number 28, which house would you run to?*

- ■ Show a number line with the multiples of 10 marked clearly. Call out other numbers, e.g. 23, 69, 48, 33, and ask children to say between which two multiples of 10 the number lies and then which is closer. They should also be introduced to the convention that equidistant numbers, in this case those ending in 5, are always rounded upwards, so 25 rounds to 30. These numbers should be avoided until children are confidently rounding other numbers.

- ■ Provide children with 0–100 number lines to help them check their answers, and for question 3, where they explore numbers that round to 30.

Things to say and ask
- ❏ *What does 53 round to? Why? What about 67? And 45?*
- ❏ *If a number rounds to 50, rather than 40 or 60, what could it be?*
- ❏ *If there are 34 chairs in this room, which ten does it round to?*
- ❏ *If there are <u>about</u> 40 children in the hall, how many might there be exactly?*

Answers

1

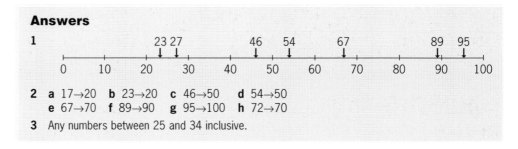

2 **a** 17→20 **b** 23→20 **c** 46→50 **d** 54→50
   e 67→70 **f** 89→90 **g** 95→100 **h** 72→70
3 Any numbers between 25 and 34 inclusive.

Finding halves

Activity Sheet 27

Objective

❏ Begin to recognise and find one half of shapes and small numbers of objects.

Vocabulary

part, equal parts,
equal groups, one half

Resources
20 counters (per child)
flashcard showing 'one half' and $\frac{1}{2}$ (per group)

Teaching support

The key idea is that halving means splitting a group of objects into two parts of equal amount. Only even numbers of objects can be grouped into halves.

Children should have a sound knowledge of numbers to 20 and preferably beyond, odd and even numbers, equality and equal parts.

Misconceptions

Children who have not grasped the concept that halves must be equally sized will need more practical experiences with specific language work.

▪ Encourage both 'grouping' and 'sharing' equally as ways of working out halves. Using the language of division when teaching fractions will help cement the concept that to find a fraction of something, it is divided or shared into equal parts.

▪ Ask children doing question 1 whether they are halving 'odd' or 'even' quantities. Reinforce the concept that an even number can be halved into whole numbers with nothing left over, e.g. half of 6 is 3, whereas half of 7 is $3\frac{1}{2}$.

▪ In question 2, encourage children to work logically so that they can see and develop patterns. For those children who can extend their work beyond finding half of 20, make sure that they continue with 22, 24, 26, 28, etc. rather than working randomly.

▪ Show children how to write 'one half' as $\frac{1}{2}$ and display the flashcard.

Things to say and ask

❏ *How many zebras are in each group? Could you halve them a different way?*
❏ *Question 2 a–c: Can you see any patterns in the numbers? Can you describe them?*

Answers

1 Remember that there is more than one way of showing the objects grouped into halves: the rings do not have to be drawn round the left-hand side of the group.
   a 1   **b** 4   **c** 2   **d** 6, 3
2 **a** 5   **b** 6   **c** 7   **d** 8, 9, 10

Finding quarters

Objective

❑ Begin to recognise and find one quarter of shapes and small numbers of objects.

Vocabulary

one quarter, group, share, equal, equally, numbers

Resources
40 counters (per child)
flashcard showing 'one quarter' and $\frac{1}{4}$ (per group)

Teaching support

The key idea is that when splitting a group of objects into quarters, the four parts must be of equal amount.

Children should have a sound knowledge of numbers to 30 and preferably to 50, and odd and even numbers. They will also need experience of sharing objects into more than two equal groups.

■ Encourage both 'grouping' and 'sharing' as ways of working out quarters. Using the language of division when teaching fractions will help cement the concept that to find a fraction of something, it is divided into equal parts.

■ Teach the strategy of halving, then halving again, to find one quarter of a set. Help children to make the connection between one half and two quarters.

■ In question 2, encourage children to work logically so that they can see and develop patterns. For those children who can extend their work beyond finding one quarter of 40, make sure that they continue with 44, 48, 52, 56, etc. rather than working randomly.

■ Show children how to write 'one quarter' as $\frac{1}{4}$ and display the flashcard.

Things to say and ask

❑ *Does it matter which parrots you ring to show one quarter?*
❑ *Question 2 a–d: Can you see any patterns in the numbers? Can you describe them?*

Answers

1	**a**	1		**b**	2					
2	**a**	3		**b**	4	**c**	5	**d**	6	**e** 7, 8, 9, 10

Half puzzles / Quarter puzzles

Objective

❑ Begin to recognise and find one half and one quarter of shapes and small numbers of objects.

Vocabulary

one half, halves, one quarter, two quarters, equal parts, divided

Resources
cut-out shapes, same size as on Activity Sheets 29 and 30 (per child)
colouring pencils

Teaching support

Misconceptions

Some children have difficulty recognising fractions when the shapes are in different orientations.

The key idea is that when dividing a shape into halves it is split into two equal parts, and when dividing a shape into quarters it is split into four equal parts.

Children will need experience of equality and equal parts, including the concept of sharing equally. They should also have done plenty of work with squares, circles and rectangles: fitting them together, moving them in and out of various arrangements and talking about what they are doing.

- Many experiences of matching, folding and shading halves should be given. Young children need concrete experiences that enable them to compare the sizes of fractional parts manually, visually and orally. The cut-out shapes should therefore be the same size as the shapes on the Activity Sheet.
- For Activity Sheet 29, you may want to cut a rectangle along a diagonal to prove that the 2 parts in question 1c are equal.
- When using Activity Sheet 30, check that children make the connection between halves and quarters: establish that one quarter is half of one half and that two quarters make one half.

Things to say and ask

- For Activity Sheet 29: *Is your coloured half of the square the same size as the white (unshaded) half? How do you know?*
- *What is the name of this shape? Do you think the two parts are halves? How have you found out?*
- For Activity Sheet 30: *Is your coloured quarter of the square the same size as each of the white quarters? How do you know?*
- *What is the name of this shape? Do you think the four parts are quarters? How did you find out?*
- *Are your quarter circles the same size?*

Answers

Activity Sheet 29: **1 a** 1st, 3rd and 4th shapes are divided into equal parts.
b 3rd and 5th shapes are divided into equal parts.
c 1st and 2nd shapes are divided into equal parts.
d 1st and 5th shapes are divided into equal parts.

Activity Sheet 30: **1 a** 1st, 2nd and 3rd shapes are divided into equal parts.
b 2nd and 4th shapes are divided into equal parts.
c 1st and 4th shapes are divided into equal parts.
d 1st shape is divided into equal parts.

Halves and quarters

Activity Sheet 31

Objective

Vocabulary

fraction, one half, two halves, one quarter, two... three... four quarters, one whole

- Begin to recognise that two halves or four quarters make one whole and that two quarters and one half are equivalent.

Resources
logic blocks

Teaching support

The key idea is that halves and quarters are called fractions, and that they can be fitted together to make whole shapes.

Children will need experience of equality and equal parts, including the concept of sharing equally. They should also have been introduced to the previous objective 'Begin to recognise and find one half and one quarter of shapes and small numbers of objects' and be used to talking about what they are doing.

- It is helpful to remind the children that one quarter is half of one half. Using the logic blocks, the children should be given some time to explore how two quarters are equivalent to one half.
- It may also be useful to have equivalent logic blocks for the children to make into squares.
- It is often difficult for children to see that the rectangular half and triangular half of a square are the same size. To demonstrate this, make an enlarged copy of both types of half, then fit the rectangle on top of the triangle and cut off the overhanging square, as shown. Cut this in half diagonally and place the pieces on the remaining gaps. (By all means talk about cutting shapes 'in half' and then 'in half again' but don't explain that the smallest pieces are eighths!)

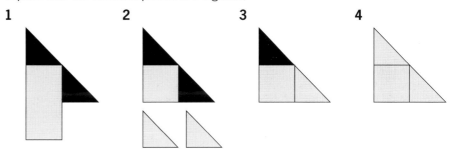

Things to say and ask

- *Do you think there are any other ways of fitting halves and quarters together to make a square?*
- *How many more can you find?*
- *How many halves will cover a square?*
- *How many quarters will cover a square?*
- *If you already have one half in the square, how many quarters do you need to cover it?*

Answers

1 a half **b** quarter **c** two, one **d** four, quarter

More halves and quarters

Activity Sheet 32

Objective

Vocabulary

- Begin to recognise that two halves or four quarters make one whole and that two quarters and one half are equivalent.

fraction, one half, halves, one quarter, quarters, the same size, equal parts, one whole

Resources
enlarged cut-out fraction cards from the top of the Activity Sheet (per child)
(You may wish to keep these cards for the game on Activity Sheet 33.)
logic blocks (per child)
blank dice labelled $\frac{1}{2}, \frac{1}{2}, \frac{1}{4}, \frac{1}{4}, \frac{2}{4}, \frac{2}{4}$ (per pair)

Misconception

Children who still find it difficult to recognise the equivalence between halves and quarters would benefit from extra practical support with blocks.

The key idea is that halves and quarters are called fractions, and that they can be fitted together to make whole shapes.

Children should have a sound knowledge of numbers to 20 and preferably beyond, and odd and even numbers. They will need experience of equality and equal parts, including the concept of sharing equally. They should also have been introduced to the previous objective 'Begin to recognise and find one half and one quarter of shapes and small numbers of objects' and be used to talking about what they are doing.

- In question 1, children use cut-out cards to make as many connections as possible. Remind them of the equivalence between halves and quarters and using the vocabulary 'the same size'. They record their findings on the Activity Sheet.

- It would be useful to have equivalent logic block pieces for the children to use.

Things to say and ask

- *How many cards can you match the 'one half' card to?*

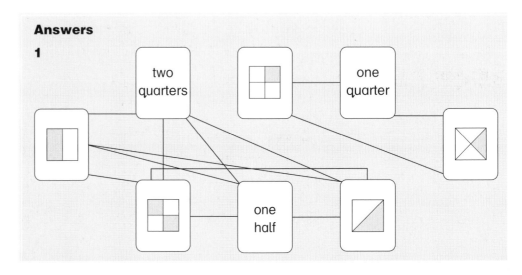

Practising with fractions / More practice with fractions

Activity Sheets 33 and 34

Objective

Vocabulary

fraction, one half, halves, one quarter, quarters, 'the same size', equal parts, one whole

- Begin to recognise that two halves or four quarters make one whole and that two quarters and one half are equivalent.

Resources

for Activity Sheet 33: 2 sets of cut-out fraction cards from Activity Sheet 32 (per pair)

for Activity Sheet 34: blank dice labelled $\frac{1}{4}, \frac{1}{2}, \frac{2}{4}, \frac{1}{4}, \frac{1}{2}, \frac{2}{4}$ (per pair)

coloured fraction pieces (see below) (per child)

The key idea is that halves and quarters can be fitted together to make whole shapes.

Children will need experience of equality and equal parts, including the concept of sharing equally. They should also have completed Activity Sheets 31 and 32, as this work consolidates those activities.

- ▢ It is important to emphasise children's acquisition of mathematical vocabulary, so the first part of Activity Sheet 33 extends the matching activity from Activity Sheet 32. (This is further extended in Activity Sheet 34.)
- ▢ Make sure the children shuffle the cards well before they start the game on Activity Sheet 33.
- ▢ To make the fraction pieces for Activity Sheet 34, photocopy the large blank squares on the sheet twice onto thin yellow card and twice onto thin blue card. Cut out the squares. Cut one yellow square into rectangular halves and the other into triangular halves. Cut one blue square into square quarters and the other into triangular quarters.
- ▢ For the children to gain full benefit from the games on both sheets, some adult support would be helpful whilst they play.

Things to say and ask

- ❑ *How many quarters make one whole?*
- ❑ *Can you tell me how to spell 'half'?*

Answers
Activity Sheet 33:
| **1** | **a** whole | **b** whole | **c** quarters | **d** half |

Activity Sheet 34:
| **1** | **a** one half | **b** one quarter | **c** one half | **d** one quarter |

Understanding addition

Activity Sheet 35

Objectives

Vocabulary

add, addition, altogether, more, plus, make, sum, total, equals

- ❑ Extend understanding of the operation of addition.
- ❑ Use and begin to read the related vocabulary.
- ❑ Use the + and = signs to record mental additions in a number sentence.
- ❑ Know by heart all addition facts for each number to at least 10.
- ❑ Use knowledge that addition can be done in any order to do mental calculations more efficiently.

Resources
flashcards with the key vocabulary
two 0–9 dice or two sets of 0–9 digit cards (per pair)
a red and a blue pencil (per pair)
practical apparatus, e.g. cubes or counters or a 0–20 number line (per child)

Teaching support

Misconceptions

When counting on to perform additions using a number line, children may begin on the wrong number. For example, with 6 + 3 children may say *six, seven, eight* rather than *seven, eight, nine*. Encourage them to appreciate that it is the jumps they are counting, rather than the numbers themselves.

The key idea is to extend children's knowledge of mathematical vocabulary associated with addition.

Children should already be familiar with the addition sign and adding numbers to 10.

- ❑ Write a statement such as 4 + 7 = 11. Invite a child to choose a flashcard and to say a sentence that describes the statement using the word, e.g. *four plus seven equals eleven.*
- ❑ In question 1, encourage children to say each question aloud, to practise using the key vocabulary.
- ❑ If necessary, children should be given practical apparatus to help them answer the questions.
- ❑ For the game ensure children realise they both work on the same sheet. Ask each child to say the questions aloud as they play, e.g. *five plus seven makes twelve.*
- ❑ Encourage children to use strategies such as counting on from the larger number.
- ❑ For question 2, encourage children to be systematic in finding addition sums with the answer 12. Can they find more than 6?

Things to say and ask

- ❑ *Say the question aloud as you add the two numbers on the dice, e.g. five plus seven makes twelve, six add three is nine. How could you write that sum down?*
- ❑ *How did you work that out? How could you do it another way? Which number did you start from?*

Answers

1	a	9	b	11	c	13
	d	15	e	15	f	14

2   Child's own answers.

Missing numbers

Activity Sheet 36

Objectives

Vocabulary

add, addition, altogether, more, plus, make, sum, total, equals, missing number, symbol

- ❑ Use the + and = signs to record mental additions in a number sentence, and recognise the use of a symbol such as ❑ or △ to stand for an unknown number.
- ❑ Choose and use appropriate operations and efficient mental strategies to solve problems.
- ❑ Use mental addition to solve simple word problems involving numbers in 'real life', using one or two steps.
- ❑ Explain how a problem was solved orally.

Resources
0–50 number line (per child)

Teaching support

Misconceptions

Children are likely to experience greater difficulty where the missing number is part of the question, particularly where it begins the question. Children may simply add the two numbers they can see. Discussing the situation and modelling it with cubes can help children to use the word 'something' wherever they see a number is missing, e.g. *fourteen subtract something is five.*

Things to say and ask

The key idea is that the equals sign is a symbol which denotes equality; it is not an instruction to give an answer.

Children need to realise that addition statements can have a missing number in any position, not simply after the equals sign.

- ❏ If children have difficulty with question 1 f–i, discuss the situation, model it with cubes and suggest using the word 'something' to stand for the missing number, e.g. *six add something equals twenty.*
- ❏ Encourage children to use the number line and to count on from the larger number.
- ❏ For question 2, children can be asked to write the situation as a number sentence. They could also draw pictures for display to represent the number sentences, e.g. drawing 16 birds + 4 birds for 16 + 4 = 20.
- ❏ Ask children to explain how they solved the word problems, e.g. *Did you count on? Did you use an addition fact that you already knew? Did you use a number line?*

- ❏ *How did you work this out?*
- ❏ *Did you use a number line?*
- ❏ *Did you count on from the larger number?*
- ❏ *How many cats are on the mat if, after 9 more sit down, there are now 17?*
- ❏ *Can you make up your own questions like these?*

Answers

1	b	29	c	23	d	27	e	22	f	14	g	20
	h	6	i	20								
2	a	20	b	18	c	8	d	7	e	11	f	9

Adding more than two numbers

Activity Sheet 37

Objectives

Vocabulary

add, addition, altogether, more, plus, make, sum, total, equals, missing number

- ❏ Understand that more than two numbers can be added.
- ❏ Begin to add three single-digit numbers mentally (totals up to about 20) or three 2-digit numbers with the help of apparatus (totals up to 100).
- ❏ Add three small numbers by putting the largest number first and/or find a pair totalling 10.
- ❏ Choose and use appropriate operations and efficient calculation strategies to solve problems.
- ❏ Repeat addition in a different order.
- ❏ Solve mathematical problems or puzzles.

Resources

practical apparatus, e.g. cubes, counters (optional) (per child)
0–9 digit cards (per child)
3 dice (per child)

The key idea is that more than two numbers can be added together, and that the order in which they are added does not affect the answer.

Children should have a sound knowledge of a range of addition facts to 10 to enable them to tackle adding three numbers more easily. They also need to appreciate that the equals sign is a symbol that denotes equality rather than being an instruction to give an answer.

- Counting apparatus can be useful to model the situation for totals above 20.
- 0–9 digit cards may be used to revise addition facts to 10, e.g. 3 + 7, 4 + 6. Encourage children to use known facts to help them find new facts, e.g. if they know that 5 + 5 is 10 then 5 + 7 is 2 more than this.
- Always ask children to explain how they worked out the answer. In question 1, ensure they are using an efficient strategy, such as looking for pairs that make 10 or starting with the largest number.
- Discuss all the answers to question 4. Compile a list of different sets of three numbers with a total of 20.
- Children should be encouraged to go back and check their answers to question 1 by adding the numbers in a different order, e.g. if they added 6 and 4 first, then 5, they can try adding 6 and 5, then 4, this time.

Things to say and ask

- *How did you work it out? Is there another way? Which number facts that you already know could help you to work this out?*
- For question 3: *How many different possible answers do you think there are?*

Answers

1	**a**	15	**b**	13	**c**	21	**d**	22	**e**	21	**f**	17

2 a 5, 12, 7 **b** 6, 4, 14

3 a 10, 30, 60 **b** 50, 20, 30

4 Any 3 numbers with a total of 20.

Near doubles

Activity Sheet 38

Objectives

Vocabulary

double, doubling, near double, less than, more than, twice

- Identify near doubles using doubles already known.
- Use patterns of similar calculations.
- Choose and use appropriate operations and efficient calculation strategies to solve problems.
- Solve mathematical problems or puzzles.

Resources
1–9 digit cards (per group)

Teaching support

Misconceptions

Children sometimes correctly identify which double a number is near to, but then get confused about which two numbers add to make this number, e.g. *Which near doubles add to make 17?* They may know that 8 + 8 = 16 but then become confused as to whether the addition is 8 + 9 or 8 + 7.

The key idea is that children appreciate the link between doubles facts they know and numbers close to these doubles, e.g. they know that 6 + 7 = 13 since 6 + 6 = 12.

Children should have a sound knowledge of the meaning of the word 'double'. It may be useful for them to have revised doubling using Activity Sheet 58: Doubles and halves. Alternatively, pick a card from a set of 1–9 digit cards and ask children to double it, or hide a card and say its double, asking them to guess the number on the card.

- To revise doubles, list the doubles for numbers to 15: 2, 4, 6, 8, 10, 12, 14, …30. Ask: *Which number is doubled to give the answer 24?* Establish that these doubles are all even numbers.

- Question 2 invites children to explore the number that is one more or one less than a double. Ensure children notice that their answers are all odd.

- For question 3, encourage children to ask themselves, e.g. *Which doubles answer is close to this number? Is this number close to 24 (double 12)? Is it one more or one less than this number?* Encourage them to appreciate that odd numbers lie between two doubles, e.g. 23 is between double 11 = 22 and double 12 = 24. Both facts could be used to help solve the question.

Things to say and ask

- *How did you work it out? Is there another way? How did you decide whether to add or subtract?*
- *Which doubles answer is close to this number?*
- *Which other double is it close to?*
- *Is this number close to e.g. 16 (double 8)? Is it one more or one less than this number?*

Answers

1 **a** 24   **b** 26   **c** 28
2 Possible answers: 41, 39; 25, 23; 13, 11; 15, 13; 31, 29; 29, 27; 9, 7; 23, 21; 17, 15; 27, 25; 19, 17
3 **a** 8, 9   **b** 12, 11   **c** 12, 13   **d** 15, 16

Adding in your head

Activity Sheet 39

Objectives

Vocabulary

count on, larger, ones, units, tens, add, plus, total, sum, altogether

- Recognise that addition can be done in any order.

- Investigate a general statement about familiar numbers by finding examples to satisfy it.

- Use knowledge that addition can be done in any order to do mental calculations more efficiently: put the larger number first and count on in 10s or 1s.

- Use the + and = signs to record mental additions in a number sentence.

Resources

0–100 number line (per group)
1–10 dice (per pair)
10–40 number cards (per pair)

Teaching support

The key idea is that once children appreciate that addition can be done in any order, they can use a counting on strategy for addition starting with the larger number.

Children should have a sound knowledge of addition facts to 10, and be familiar with the addition sign.

▢ Write: 'Numbers can be added in any order. The answer is the same'. Read this to the children and ask: *Is this true? How could we find out?* Encourage them to suggest how this statement could be checked, and to give examples. Demonstrate on a 0–100 number line, e.g. how counting on 23 from 5 gives the same answer as counting on 5 from 23. *Which is the quicker way?* Discuss how starting with the larger number and counting on a small number can be done in your head or using fingers.

▢ Encourage children to put the number 23 'in their head' and count on 5. Give further examples, e.g. 6 + 18, and invite children to count on without the number line. Where possible discuss using known number facts, e.g. 3 + 25: *I want to count on 3 from 25 and I know that 5 + 3 is 8, so the answer must be 28.*

▢ For the game, children could stop after a given time interval, or when they have written four pairs of number sentences, for example.

▢ Once a range of addition sentences has been recorded for the game, ask further questions, e.g. *How did knowing that adding can be done in any order help you? Which was your largest total? How did you work it out?*

Things to say and ask

❑ *How did you find the answer? Why did you do it that way? Is there an easier way?*
❑ *Can you try it without a number line?*

Answers

1	a	28	b	28	c	39	d	40	e	33	f	42
	g	90	h	80	i	90						
2	a	33	b	44	c	32	d	38				

Splitting numbers

Activity Sheet 40

Objectives

Vocabulary

units, ones, tens, add, addition, split

❑ Partition into '5 and a bit' when adding 6, 7, 8 or 9, then recombine.

❑ Partition additions into tens and units then recombine.

❑ Choose and use appropriate operations and efficient calculation strategies to solve problems.

❑ Solve simple word problems involving money and find totals.

Resources
none

Teaching support

The key idea is that children are encouraged to partition 6, 7, 8 and 9 into '5 and a bit' when adding. This can help them to add mentally by splitting numbers into parts that are easy to add.

A familiarity with coins is useful for this activity.

▢ Begin by asking children to split the numbers 6 to 9 into '5 and a bit', e.g. *8 is 5 and how many more?* Record these, e.g. *8 = 5 + 3*. Establish how this can be useful, e.g. when adding 8 to 5: 5 + 8: 5 + 5 + 3 = 10 + 3 = 13

▢ It is important to explain to children how to use the coins to answer question 1. Show children how to look at the question and then at the coins, e.g. 6p + 7p is the same as two 5p coins and three 1p coins. *Two 5p coins is 10p and 3 more makes 13p.*

▢ In question 2, children find different ways to spend up to 14p. Tell children that they do not have to spend all of the 14p.

▢ For question 3, discuss how numbers can be partitioned into tens and units to add, and ensure children understand how to use the coins to help them.

Things to say and ask

❑ *How did you do this question? Did you split the numbers up? How did you split them?*
❑ *How much change would you be given from 14p if you bought those two sweets?*

Answers

1 **b** 15p   **c** 15p   **d** 14p
   e 24p   **f** 22p   **g** 33p   **h** 31p

2 Possible answers: 5p + 6p, 6p + 6p, 5p + 7p, 6p + 7p, 5p + 8p, 7p + 7p, 6p + 8p, 5p + 9p

3 Possible answers: 25p: 11p + 14p, 12p + 13p; 24p: 11p + 13p, 12p + 12p; 26p: 12p + 14p, 13p + 13p; 27p: 14p + 13p

Pairing numbers

Activity Sheet 41

Objectives

Vocabulary

units, ones, tens, hundred, add, addition, plus, more, makes, altogether, total, sum, pair, multiple

❑ Know by heart: all addition facts for each number to 10;
                 all pairs of numbers with a total of 20;
                 all pairs of multiples of 10 with a total of 100.

❑ Repeat addition in a different order.

Resources
1–10 number cards (per group)
colouring pencils (per child)
1–20 dice (per pair)
20 counters (per pair)

Teaching support

Misconceptions

Some children find memorising number facts difficult and should be encouraged to try to learn them at home as well as at school. It can help to build on a known fact to learn other related facts, e.g. if they know 5 + 5 = 10 then they could try to learn related addition facts such as 6 + 5, 7 + 5, 6 + 6, etc.

The key idea is for children to develop speed of recall, rather than using apparatus (including fingers) to find answers. Encourage children to make use of the facts they know by heart to help derive other facts.

Children should be developing a sound knowledge of a range of addition facts without needing to 'work it out'.

- Give each child a 1–10 number card. Call out two children's names and ask them to stand, holding their number cards for all to see. The winner is the child standing who gives the correct total first. The other child sits and a new name is called to create a new addition question. In this game, children can be encouraged to focus on their number and think of questions they might face.

- As a further activity, children can check their answers to question 2 by adding the numbers in a different order.

Things to say and ask

- ❏ *How did you find the answer? Did you know it in your head?*
- ❏ *Did you use a different fact to help you?*

Answers

1

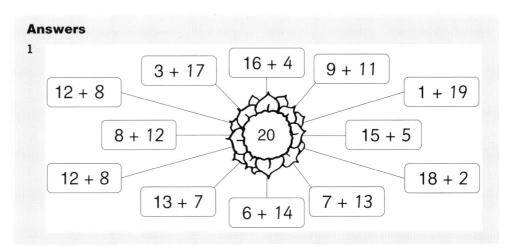

Adding and subtracting

Activity Sheet 42

Objectives

Vocabulary

add, addition, more, pair, subtract, take away, minus, less

- ❏ Extend understanding of the operation of subtraction.

- ❏ Use and begin to read the related vocabulary.

- ❏ Understand that subtraction is the inverse of addition (subtraction reverses addition).

Resources

0–20 number line (per group)

counter (per group)

0–9 digit cards (2 sets per pair)

Teaching support

The key idea is to develop an understanding of subtraction as the inverse of addition, and vice versa. The use of number lines or strips allows children to count forwards and backwards in order to see that addition and subtraction 'undo' each other, e.g. 15 + 7 = 22 and 22 − 7 = 15.

Children should already be familiar with the addition and subtraction signs. They should also have a sound understanding of addition as combining sets together and of counting along a number line, and of subtraction as taking away or finding the difference.

◾ Ask questions counting on or back along a horizontal 0–20 number line, e.g. *I start on the number 6 and add 5 to it, then I subtract 2, then add 4, etc.* Use a counter to follow the chain. Remind children that adding numbers moves the counter to the right, towards larger numbers, and subtraction moves it to the left, towards smaller numbers. Encourage children to follow the chain, predicting where the counter will move to each time. *How did you know it would end up at 18? Did you know a number fact? Which one? Could you have used a different one?*

◾ Give a question in which children add and then subtract the same number, e.g. *13 add 6, then subtract 6.* Ask children to explain what they notice. Encourage them to realise that subtracting a number can 'undo' an addition of that same number. Write an addition question, e.g. 12 + 6 =, and ask them to solve it. Now write 18 − 6 =. *Can you say what the answer is, using the addition question to help you?* Demonstrate this on the number line. *You can use addition questions to help you answer subtraction questions.*

◾ When children have completed question 2, discuss the fact that the number in the head and the tail is the same, i.e. that subtraction 'undoes' addition. Children can be asked to draw their own worms.

◾ In the game, ensure children understand which 3 numbers they must use to write a subtraction sentence.

Things to say and ask

❏ *Why are these two questions grouped together? One is addition and the other is subtraction. What is special about the numbers?*
❏ *What do you notice about the numbers in the worm's head and tail? Why do you think this is?*
❏ *Make up your own questions like these.*

Answers

1	a	21, 15	b	25, 14	c	26, 18		
2	a	15	b	17	c	24	d	26

Understanding subtraction

Activity Sheet 43

Objectives

Vocabulary

subtract, take away, minus, leave, difference between

❏ Know by heart all subtraction facts for each number to at least 10.

❏ Use the − and = signs to record mental subtractions in a number sentence.

Resources
two 0–9 dice or two sets of 0–9 digit cards (per pair)
a red and a blue pencil (per pair)

Teaching support

Misconceptions

In the game, ensure children say differences correctly, e.g. if the score is a 2 and a 6, they say *six minus two equals four* not *two minus six equals four*.

Things to say and ask

The key idea is that children should develop rapid recall of subtraction facts for all numbers up to and including 10.

Children should already be familiar with the subtraction sign and subtracting numbers to 10. Question 2 requires understanding of the idea of subtraction as the difference between two numbers. Children should be aware that taking the smaller number from the larger number gives you the difference.

- Discuss strategies for finding the difference. Ensure children count on/back correctly and do not include the starting number in the count.
- Encourage children to try to know by heart the answers for subtraction facts to 10 so they do not need to work them out each time.
- Encourage children to say each part of question 1 aloud to practise using the key vocabulary.
- For the game, ensure children realise they both work on the same sheet. Ask them how they found the answer and to say a subtraction sentence.

- For the game: *Say a number sentence as you find the difference, e.g. eight minus seven makes one, nine take away six is three, the difference between nine and four is five. How could you write it down?*
- *How did you work that out? Could you do it another way? Which number did you start from?*

Answers

1 **a** 3   **b** 3   **c** 3   **d** 6   **e** 6   **f** 6
2 Child's own answers.

Find the missing numbers

Activity Sheet 44

Objectives

Vocabulary

subtract, take away, minus, leave, difference between, symbol, calculate, calculation

- Use the – and = signs to record mental subtractions in a number sentence and recognise the use of a symbol such as ❑ or △ to stand for an unknown number.
- Use and begin to read the related vocabulary.
- Choose and use appropriate operations and efficient mental strategies to solve problems.
- Use mental subtraction to solve simple word problems involving numbers in 'real life', using one or two steps.
- Explain how the problem was solved.

Resources
0–50 number line (per child)
practical apparatus, e.g. cubes or counters (optional) (per child)

Misconceptions

Children may experience difficulty where the missing number is part of the question. They may simply find the difference between (or even add) the two numbers they can see.

The key idea is that the equals sign is a symbol which denotes equality; it is not an instruction to give an answer. Children need to understand that subtraction statements can have a missing number in any position and not simply after the equals sign.

Children should understand subtraction as taking away or finding the difference.

- ❏ Encourage children to read each question aloud. This will extend their understanding of the related vocabulary.
- ❏ Children can be given practical apparatus to help them answer the questions. Discuss different strategies for solving subtraction questions using a number line, e.g. counting up from the smaller number or counting back from the larger number, and demonstrate how much quicker this is than counting out objects and removing some of them.
- ❏ For question 2, children can be asked to write the situation as a number sentence. They could also draw pictures for display to represent the number sentences, e.g. drawing groups of rabbits to show 17 − 4 = 13.
- ❏ Ask children to explain how they work out the answers to the word problems. *Did you use addition? Did you count up? Did you count back?*

- ❏ *Read these questions and answers aloud to your friend to check your work, e.g. fifteen minus four makes eleven, fourteen subtract eight is six, the difference between eighteen and five is thirteen.*
- ❏ *How did you work that out? Could you do it another way? Which number did you start from?*
- ❏ *How could you write this story down as a number sentence?*

Answers

1	**a** 11	**b** 13	**c** 6	**d** 9	**e** 3	**f** 6
2	**a** 13	**b** 12	**c** 11	**d** 12	**e** 17	**f** 11

What's the difference?

Activity Sheet 45

Vocabulary

subtract, take away, minus, leave, difference between, count up, count on, add

- ❏ Find a small difference by counting up from the smaller to the larger number.
- ❏ Use mental subtraction to solve simple word problems involving numbers in 'real life', using one or two steps.
- ❏ Check with an equivalent calculation.

Resources

0–100 number line (per group)

1–20 dice (per pair)

counters (per pair)

Misconceptions

Children sometimes start counting on at the number they are on rather than the next number, e.g. with 6 + 3 they may say *six, seven, eight rather than seven, eight, nine*. Remind them that it is the jumps they are counting, rather than the numbers themselves.

The key idea is that children practise the strategy of finding a small difference by counting up from the smaller to the larger number.

Children should have experience of subtracting a single-digit number from another single-digit number or from a 2-digit number. They should also be familiar with the vocabulary associated with subtraction, in particular 'take away', 'how many more to make' and 'difference'.

- Children need to understand that they can tackle a subtraction question using a counting up method.
- Begin by considering a subtraction such as 19 – 15. Use a 0–100 number line and write 19 – 15 on the board. *We can subtract 15 from 19 by counting back 15 from 19 (18, 17, 16, 15, … 7, 6, 5, 4) or we can find the difference between them by counting up (16, 17, 18, 19). Counting back and counting up give the same answer – it's 4. Which way do you think is easier?*
- Question 1 includes a number track for children to count along. Some children should be encouraged to work it out in their heads first and use the number track to check.
- Can children find a different way of calculating, e.g. counting back, to check some of their answers?

Things to say and ask

- *How did you do this question? What's the difference between 26 and 14?*
- *How could you write this story down as a number sentence?*

Answers

1 a 5   b 5   c 7   d 7   e 11   f 13
2 a 5p   b 6p

Adding and subtracting 9 and 11

Activity Sheet 46

Objective

- Add/subtract 9 or 11: add/subtract 10 and adjust by 1.

Vocabulary

subtract, add, addition, more, less, find all

Resources

1–100 number square

Misconceptions

Children sometimes get confused over the process of adjustment. They may be unsure whether to add or subtract 1 after adding or subtracting 10. Encourage children to think of the situation in context, e.g. *You have 23 cubes and you want to add 9 more. You add 10. You have added too many, so you then subtract 1.*

The key idea is to learn how to add and subtract 9 or 11 to and from a number, by adding or subtracting 10 and then adjusting by 1.

Children should have a sound knowledge of adding and subtracting 10 to and from a number.

- Use a 1–100 number square to help children practise counting forwards and backwards in 10s. Provide questions that add or subtract 10, e.g. 42 + 10 or 51 – 10. Show these on the number square. Discuss how the units digit remains unchanged when 10 is added or subtracted. *If we were to add ten and then take away one it is the same as adding nine.* Give some examples on the number square, e.g. 42 + 9.

- In the same way, show that adding 11 is the same as adding 10 and 1 more.

- Once children are confident with adding 9 or 11, introduce subtracting 9 or 11. Allow children to use a 1–100 number square if necessary.

- Question 3 allows children to create as many questions and answers as they can by choosing two numbers. Encourage them to be systematic in finding all the different questions and answers.

- ❏ *What is ten more/less than…?*
- ❏ *Explain how you did this question.*
- ❏ *What did you add (or subtract)?*
- ❏ *How did you know whether to add?*

Answers

1   **a**   25   **b**   8   **c**   29   **d**   28   **e**   17   **f**   43
    g   17   **h**   20   **i**   19

2   47 + 9, 56 – 11, 45 – 9, 36

3   Possible answers: 34 + 9 = 43, 21 + 9 = 30, 17 + 9 = 26;
                  25 + 11 = 36, 34 + 11 = 45, 21 + 11 = 32, 17 + 11 = 28;
                  25 – 9 = 16, 34 – 9 = 25, 21 – 9 = 12, 17 – 9 = 8;
                  25 – 11 = 14, 34 – 11 = 23, 21 – 11 = 10, 17 – 11 = 6

Adding and subtracting 19 and 21

Activity Sheet 47

Vocabulary

subtract, take away, add, find all

- ❏ Add/subtract 19 or 21: add/subtract 20 and adjust by 1.

Resources

1–100 number square (per group)

Misconceptions

Children sometimes get confused over the process of adjustment. They may be unsure whether to add or subtract 1 after adding or subtracting 10 or 20. Encourage children to think of the situation in context, e.g. *You have 34 counters and you want to take away 19. You take away 20. You have taken away too many, so you then add 1.*

The key idea is to add and subtract 19 or 21 to and from a number, by adding or subtracting 20 and then adjusting by 1.

Children should have a sound knowledge of adding and subtracting 20 to and from a number, and should be familiar with adding 9 and 11 using this strategy of adjustment.

- Use a 1–100 number square to help children practise counting forwards and backwards in 10s and 20s.
- Provide questions that add or subtract 20, e.g. 42 + 20 or 51 – 20. Show these on the number square. Discuss how the units digit remains unchanged when multiples of 10 are added or subtracted. *If we add twenty and then take away one it is the same as adding nineteen.* Give some examples on the number square, e.g. 42 + 19.
- In the same way, show that adding 21 is the same as adding 20 and 1 more.
- Once children are confident with adding 19 or 21, introduce subtracting 19 or 21. Allow children to use a 1–100 number square if necessary.
- Question 2 allows children to create as many questions and answers as they can by choosing two numbers. Encourage them to be systematic in finding all the different questions and answers.

- *What is twenty more/less than...?*
- *Explain how you did this question.*
- *What did you add (or subtract)?*
- *How did you know whether to add?*

Answers

1 **a** 39 **b** 9 **c** 46 **d** 11 **e** 46 **f** 17
   g 47 **h** 19 **i** 53

2 Possible answers: 38 + 19 = 57, 41 + 19 = 60, 56 + 19 = 75;
        27 + 21 = 48, 38 + 21 = 59, 41 + 21 = 62, 56 + 21 = 77;
        27 – 19 = 8, 38 – 19 = 19, 41 – 19 = 22, 56 – 19 = 37;
        27 – 21 = 6, 38 – 21 = 17, 41 – 21 = 20, 56 – 21 = 35

3 48, 69, 50, 71, 52

Subtractions and additions

Activity Sheet 48

- State the subtraction corresponding to a given addition, and vice versa.

Vocabulary

number sentence

Resources

up to 20 cubes or counters (per group and per child)

The key idea is that children use the relationship between addition and subtraction.

Children should have a sound knowledge of the meaning of the + and – signs. They should also understand that addition is the inverse of subtraction and vice versa.

- Begin by writing three related numbers, e.g. 3, 7 and 10. *What do you notice about these numbers? How could I use them to make a question and an answer?* Ask children to write an addition fact using these numbers: 3 + 7 = 10 or 7 + 3 = 10. Show a set of three and a set of seven and combine them to make ten. One child could hold a set of three cubes, another a set of seven and these could be combined.

- Now ask the children to give subtraction sentences using these numbers: 10 − 3 = 7 and 10 − 7 = 3. Again show this by splitting the ten items into a group of three and a group of seven.

- Encourage children to realise that, when calculating, any one of these four sentences can be used to help solve the others, e.g. if you know that 3 and 7 equals 10, then 10 minus 3 equals 7.

- Provide a new set of related numbers, e.g. 5, 3 and 8, and ask children to suggest the related facts.

- Invite children to suggest other sets of three similarly related numbers, e.g. 6, 5 and 11. Ask them to write the number sentences and to show each situation using cubes or counters.

- Question 1 encourages children to notice the relationship between addition and subtraction by placing the four related number facts together. They could be encouraged to model the situation with cubes if appropriate.

Things to say and ask

- *Why are these four questions grouped together? Two are addition and two are subtraction. What is special about them?*
- *Give me an addition fact. Can you give me a subtraction fact using the same numbers?*
- *Can you make up your own addition and subtraction questions in the same way?*

Answers

1 a   4 + 5 = **9**, 5 + 4 = **9**, 9 − 5 = **4**, 9 − 4 = **5**
   b   7 − 3 = **4**, 7 − 4 = **3**, 3 + 4 = **7**, 4 + 3 = **7**
2 a   6 + 5 = **11**, 5 + 6 = 11, 11 − 6 = 5, 11 − 5 = 6
   b   8 − 3 = **5**, 8 − 5 = **3**, 3 + 5 = **8**, 5 + 3 = **8**
3 Child's own answers.

Adding and subtracting in your head

Activity Sheet 49

Objectives

- Use known number facts and place value to add/subtract mentally, without crossing the tens boundary.

- Repeat addition in a different order.

Vocabulary

addition, subtract

Resources
none

Teaching support

Misconceptions

Questions 2 and 4 involve writing a question for a given answer. Some children may find this difficult, not knowing how to choose from a wide range of possible questions. Give them examples and, as a further activity, encourage them to write as many different questions as they can with a given answer.

The key idea is to practise adding and subtracting numbers that do not cross a 10s boundary. (See the NNS Framework, Supplement of examples: Years 1, 2 and 3 pp. 37 and 39 for details of expected outcomes.)

Children should have a sound knowledge of counting on or back in 1s or 10s. It would be useful for them to have experienced Activity Sheets 20 and 21 on place value prior to beginning this activity.

- List several addition and subtraction questions involving numbers that do not cross a 10s boundary, e.g. 23 + 6, 32 + 15, 49 − 4, 38 − 15. *What is the answer to this question? How did you work it out? Did anyone work it out a different way?* Discuss the range of strategies used, emphasising the use of recall of number facts or of partitioning numbers to add or subtract. *How can we use the fact 3 + 6 = 9 to help us answer 23 + 6? How can we split 15 to make it easier to add?* Encourage children to verbalise their thinking and to explain strategies in their own words.

- Encourage children to work through the questions without apparatus, finding answers mentally.
- As a further activity, children could go back and check their answers to question 1 by adding the numbers in a different order, e.g. if they added 3 to 16 first, then they can try adding 16 to 3 this time.

Things to say and ask

- *What is the answer to this question? How did you work it out?*
- *Did anyone work it out a different way?*
- *How can we use the fact 6 + 3 = 9 to help us answer 16 + 3?*
- *Could we use the answer to an addition fact to help us answer a subtraction fact?*

Answers

1	**b**	29	**c**	36	**d**	38	**e**	58	**f**	82
2	Child's own answers.									
3	**b**	32	**c**	62	**d**	55	**e**	25	**f**	40
	g	14	**h**	30	**i**	35				

Number towers

Activity Sheet 50

Objectives

Vocabulary

add, addition, plus, altogether, total, sum, more, pair, subtract, take away, minus, less, tens boundary

- Use known number facts and place value to add/subtract mentally.
- Bridge through 10 or 20, then adjust.
- Solve mathematical problems or puzzles.
- Suggest extensions saying 'What if...?' or 'What could I try next...?'.

Resources
0–30 number line (per group)

Teaching support

Misconceptions
It should be pointed out that question 2 involves finding the difference, rather than adding.

The key idea is to practise and develop mental addition and subtraction skills through building addition and subtraction towers. The numbers given provide practice in crossing 10 and 20, which can be used as a 'bridge'.

Children should have practised a range of strategies for addition and subtraction without crossing a tens boundary. They will need to have a sound understanding of how the towers develop before tackling the Activity Sheet.

- Use a 0–30 number line to demonstrate the process of bridging, where 10 (or 20) is used as a 'stopover', e.g. for 6 + 7: *six and four more is ten so 6 + 7 is three more than this.*
- Point to the larger number in the addition, e.g. 8 + 6, and ask: *How many more to make ten (or twenty)? If we add two more to make ten, how many more do we still need to add?* Invite a child to point to the numbers on the number line. Once children have tackled several questions of this type, e.g. 8 + 4, 7 + 5, 6 + 9, 14 + 7, remove the number line and encourage children to attempt this mentally.
- Finding the difference can also be done using a bridging method, e.g. the difference between 6 and 13 can be found by counting on 4 from 6 to make 10 and then counting on another 3, giving the difference 7.

- Encourage children to work through the Activity Sheet without apparatus, finding answers mentally. Introduce the number towers by showing how to add the adjacent numbers for question 1 and how to find the differences between adjacent numbers for question 2.
- Question 3 allows children to choose their own start numbers. Discuss the range of different towers created.
- Encourage children to extend the towers idea to create larger towers with more levels. Set specific criteria, e.g. *Can you make a four-level tower with the bottom number zero?*

Things to say and ask

- *How did you make that tower?*
- *For question 1: Are the top numbers the same as your friend's?*
- *For question 2: Are the bottom numbers the same as your friend's?*
- *How did you work it out? Did anyone work it out a different way?*

Answers

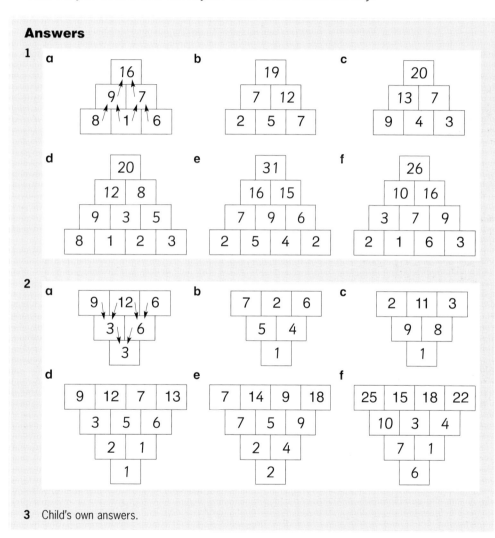

1

a
```
        16
      9    7
    8    1    6
```

b
```
        19
      7    12
    2    5    7
```

c
```
        20
      13   7
    9    4    3
```

d
```
        20
      12    8
    9    3    5
  8    1    2    3
```

e
```
        31
      16   15
    7    9    6
  2    5    4    2
```

f
```
        26
      10   16
    3    7    9
  2    1    6    3
```

2

a
```
  9   12   6
    3    6
      3
```

b
```
  7    2    6
    5    4
      1
```

c
```
  2   11    3
    9    8
      1
```

d
```
  9   12   7   13
    3    5    6
      2    1
        1
```

e
```
  7   14   9   18
    7    5    9
      2    4
        2
```

f
```
  25   15   18   22
    10    3    4
       7    1
          6
```

3 Child's own answers.

Solving simple problems

Activity Sheet 51

Objectives

Vocabulary

add, altogether, total, more, subtract, less

❑ Use mental addition and subtraction to solve problems involving numbers in 'real life' and money, using one or two steps.

❑ Explain how the problem was solved.

Resources

0–30 number line (per child)

Teaching support

Misconceptions

Some children have difficulty working out whether to add or subtract the numbers in word problems. Invite children to the front and ask them to model situations like those shown, e.g. a child might say *I had twenty-four pounds.* You ask: *How much have you spent?* to which the reply comes: *Six pounds.* The child can act out spending £6 and the subtraction can be shown on the board, e.g. 24 – 6 = 18.

The key idea is for children to develop speed of recall, rather than using apparatus (including fingers) to find the answers. Children should be encouraged to use the facts they know by heart to help derive other facts.

Children should have a sound knowledge of addition and subtraction with numbers up to 30.

◼ Children should work in pairs and read each situation aloud, where possible. Encourage them to try to work without apparatus, finding answers mentally using recall of number facts. However, some children may benefit from a 0–30 number line for counting on and back.

◼ Some children may require help reading the text on this sheet.

◼ Model money situations like those in question 2, e.g. choose a child and give him or her an amount of money. *Here is three pounds. If I give you six pounds more, how much will you have now? What if I now take three pounds from you? How much have you now?* Choose another child and explain that this child has twice as much. *How much have you got then?* Encourage children to explain whether they used addition or subtraction to find the answers and invite them to explain their strategies for working the answer out.

Things to say and ask

❑ *Did you add or subtract the numbers? How did you decide what to do?*
❑ *How did you work it out? Did anyone work it out a different way?*
❑ *How could you check if you were right?*

Answers

1	**b**	16	**c**	19	**d**	20	**e**	24	**f**	24	
2	**a**	£18	**b**	£20 ✓	**c**	£6	**d**	£7 ✓	**e**	£11	**f** £12 ✓

Recognising coins

Activity Sheet 52

Vocabulary

money, coin, pence, pound, £, p, total

❏ Recognise all coins and begin to use £·p notation for money.

❏ Find totals.

Resources
set of 8 coins (real if possible): 1p, 2p, 5p, 10p, 20p, 50p, £1, £2 (per child)

Teaching support

Misconceptions

Children often write incorrectly both £ and p when recording amounts, as in £2·25p.

Many children find recording an amount with a zero difficult, e.g. £2·05 is often recorded as £2·5 or £2·5p. The trails have been devised to avoid this problem arising. Activity Sheet 53, however, involves amounts of this type.

The key idea is that children demonstrate their ability to recognise all coins by placing them on the spaces shown. They then follow trails from start to finish through a series of coins. They choose their own paths, record the coins they pass and find the totals.

Children should already be familiar with the different coins and know their names when shown.

▨ Revise the coins by holding each up and asking children to say its value. *Which coins are silver? Which coin is worth the most? the least?*

▨ Discuss how e.g. a 5p coin is smaller than a 2p coin, although it is worth more.

▨ Ask children to calculate simple totals of coins and show how these can be written, e.g. 52p, £1·50, £2·15. Give plenty of examples and explain to children that when writing an amount in pounds and pence there should be two numbers after the point.

▨ For question 2, make sure children realise that they should only use each coin once on a trail. All trails should be at least four coins long.

Things to say and ask

❏ *How did you get that total? Which way did you go?*
❏ *What was the largest total you got?*
❏ *What was the smallest?*
❏ *Which route went through most coins?*
❏ *Was this the largest total?*

Answers

2 Possible route totals with four coins: 77p, £2·23, £2·72
With five coins: 87p, 78p, £1·37, £1·77, £2·77
With six coins: £1·87, £1·78, £2·78, £2·83, £3·37, £3·77
With seven coins: £1·88, £2·88, £3·83, £3·78, £3·87
With eight coins: £3·88

3 £3·88

4 77p

Finding totals and using coins

Activity Sheet 53

Vocabulary

money, coin, pence, pound, £, p, total, change, price, cheap, dear, fewest, fewer

❏ Recognise all coins and begin to use £·p notation for money.

❏ Find totals and work out which coins to pay.

❏ Solve mathematical problems or puzzles.

Resources

set of 8 coins (real if possible): 1p, 2p, 5p, 10p, 20p, 50p, £1, £2 (per child)

Teaching support

Misconceptions

Many children find recording an amount with a zero difficult, e.g. £2·05 is often recorded as £2·5 or £2·5p. Give plenty of examples and emphasise that when writing an amount in pounds and pence there should be two numbers after the point. This activity involves amounts of this type.

The key idea is for children to find totals involving coins and work out the smallest number of coins needed to buy a given total.

Children should have a sound knowledge of coin values and be familiar with ways of recording money in pounds and pence.

■ Revise finding totals of sets of coins.

■ Some children may find question 1 easier if they place actual coins on the outlines (you may want to enlarge the sheet to A3). These can then be moved and arranged as desired.

■ Encourage children to start with the largest coins, e.g. *10p and two fives makes 20p, then add the two and the one to make 23p.*

■ In question 3, children should list the coins and record the amount. They can be told to use only one of each type of coin, e.g. £1 + 1p + 1p would not be allowed. Discuss the range of possible prices for the dinosaur and compile a list. *What is the most that the dinosaur could have cost? What is the least?*

Things to say and ask

❏ *Which purse has the largest total? How did you work it out?*
❏ *Think about using a 20p in this question. Could you make this total using fewer coins?*
❏ *What other prices could the dinosaur have been?*

Answers

1 a 23p   b £1·87   c £3·81
2 (Answers are provided for the smallest numbers of coins, though other answers are possible:)
   b 50p, 20p, 10p, 5p   c £1, 2p, 2p   d £2, 5p, 2p
3 (Multiple answers are possible.)

Giving change

Objectives

Vocabulary

£, p, total, change, bought, sold, jottings

❑ Recognise all coins and begin to use £·p notation for money.

❑ Give change and work out which coins to pay.

❑ Solve mathematical problems or puzzles.

Resources
0–50 number line

set of 8 coins (real if possible): 1p, 2p, 5p, 10p, 20p, 50p, £1, £2 (per child)

Teaching support

The key idea is for children to appreciate that giving change is an important concept when dealing with money. Children need to realise that they can work out the change by either subtracting or counting up.

Children should have a sound knowledge of coin values and be familiar with ways of recording money in pounds and pence.

▪ Write some prices of items, e.g. a ball costing 38p. Ask children to work out how much change from 50p would be given when buying each one. Children can be introduced to a counting up method for finding and giving change. *The ball costs 38p and you pay by giving a 50p coin. To find the change count on 2p to get to 40p, then another 10p to get to 50p. You counted on 2p, then 10p so the change will be 12p.* Demonstrate on a 0–50 number line and show children how to use jottings to support their mental calculation. Coins can be handed over by a chosen 'shopkeeper'.

▪ For question 2, give children a set of coins and explain that three of the coins have been handed over as change from £1. Ask them to work out how much the fish must have cost for each set of three coins. Encourage them to find as many possibilities as they can.

Things to say and ask

❑ *How did you work out the amount of change?*
❑ *What if you were given a 50p coin in your change?*
❑ *Which three coins could have been given in change?*
❑ *Did you use a counting on method?*

Answers
1 **b** 11p   **c** 25p   **d** 9p   **e** 22p   **f** 14p
2 (Multiple answers are possible.)

Begin to multiply

Activity Sheet 55

Vocabulary

lots of, groups of, multiply, repeated addition, times as, row, column

❑ Understand the operation of multiplication as repeated addition.

❑ Use and begin to read the related vocabulary.

❑ Use the $\times$ and $=$ signs to record mental calculations in a number sentence.

Resources
about 5 number cards showing the number 10

Teaching support

Misconceptions

Children may initially add rather than multiply when faced with '4 $\times$ 3' or '4 lots of 3', for example, giving the answer 7 rather than 12. This may imply they haven't yet understood the nature of multiplication or may more simply be a result of seeing the '$\times$' sign as '+'.

Multiplication can be understood in two ways, for example 4 $\times$ 3 can be interpreted as 'four lots of three', (the approach taken here) or as '3 multiplied by 4'. Both are valid, and the result is the same. Children will need to develop an appreciation of the two, together with the associated language, but the first approach is often more easily understood at this stage. Check your school policy to ensure a consistent approach.

The key idea is to introduce multiplication as repeated addition, i.e. that $2 + 2 + 2$ is the same as three lots of 2 or 3×2.

Children should have a good understanding of addition and be confident at counting on in 2s, 5s and 10s.

◼ Begin by counting on in twos from zero.

◼ Explain to the children that you want to count the number of ears of several children. Point to each child as a number is spoken, e.g. two, four, six, eight... When five children have been pointed to, ask *How many ears have these five children altogether? Five lots of two is..?* Repeat the counting in twos to find the answer ten.

◼ Count other parts of the body such as hands, e.g. choose 6 children and ask *How many hands have these six children? Six lots of two is…?*

◼ Once several counts have been made, start to record on the board. 6 lots of $2 = 2 + 2 + 2 + 2 + 2 + 2 = 12$. Discuss the fact that this is rather lengthy and introduce the $\times$ sign. Write 6×2 and explain that this sign is used to mean 'lots of' or 'groups of'. Ask children to say aloud *Six lots of two.* Again, find the answer to six lots of two by adding (counting on) two, then another two, then another two etc..

◼ Count on in tens from zero.

◼ Write 4×10 on the board. Explain this means four lots of ten or four groups of ten. Choose four children to hold number cards showing the number 10. Ask them to count aloud in tens as each number card is pointed to, e.g. 10, 20, 30, 40.

◼ Write other multiplication questions, e.g. 3×10, 2×10, 5×10 and ask children to read them aloud and solve them. Continue to make the link between repeated addition and multiplication.

Things to say and ask

❑ *What does this (4 $\times$ 3) mean?*
❑ *How do we say it? How many is four lots of three?*
❑ *What is the same as three add three add three add three?*
❑ *How many lots of beetles/worms are here? How many beetles/worms are in each lot/group? How many is that altogether?*

Answers

1 a $4 \times 2 = 8$ b $3 \times 2 = 6$ c $5 \times 2 = 10$ b $7 \times 2 = 14$
2 a 2, $2 \times 10 = 20$ b 3, $3 \times 10 = 30$ c 5, $5 \times 10 = 50$
3 a 30   b 16

More multiplying

Activity Sheet 56

Vocabulary

array, row, column, times, multiply, multiplied by

❏ Understand the operation of multiplication as describing an array.

❏ Use and begin to read the related vocabulary.

Resources
a red and a blue pencil (per child)
about 24 counters (per pair)

Misconceptions

Children can find arranging counters in an array difficult. Ensure children realise that there must be the same number of counters in each row and in each column.

The key idea is to introduce the idea of multiplication as describing an array. Arrays are useful as they can help children to appreciate the commutative nature of multiplication, that is, that multiplication can be done in any order, e.g. 3×2 gives the same answer as 2×3.

Children should be familiar with the $\times$ sign as meaning 'lots of' or 'groups of'. They should be confident at counting on in 2s, 3s, 4s, 5s and 10s.

▪ Introduce (or revise) the terms row and column. Draw a simple array of dots with 3 rows of 4 on the board. Ask children to suggest how they could find out how many there are. Discuss that all could be counted but encourage children to think of a quicker way. *How many are in the first row? (4) How many rows? (3).* Ask children to count on in fours three times to give 12. Show how this can also be done by counting the number in one column (3) and then finding the number of columns (4). Ask children to count on in threes four times.

▪ Show how the two ways of counting the array can be represented using the multiplication symbol $\times$, e.g. 3×4 and 4×3. Describe these as 3 lots of 4 and 4 lots of 3. Discuss how the answer is the same whichever way it is written or calculated.

▪ Demonstrate how counters can be used to make an array. Ensure children realise that there must be the same number of counters in each row and in each column. If appropriate, some children could be asked to describe the array as a multiplication question, e.g. 2 rows of 3 as 2×3.

❏ *How many counters are in the first row?*
❏ *How many rows are there?*
❏ *How many counters are in the first column?*
❏ *How many columns are there?*
❏ *How could we write this using the $\times$ sign?*

Answers

1 a/b

c $5 \times 3 = 15$ $3 \times 5 = 15$

2 a/b

c $4 \times 5 = 20$ $5 \times 4 = 20$

Multiplication puzzles

Activity Sheet 57

Objectives

Vocabulary

twice, three times, four times, … multiply, multiplied by

❑ Know by heart multiplication facts for the 2 and 10 times-tables.

❑ Begin to know multiplication facts for the 5 times-table.

❑ Recognise the use of a symbol such as ❑ or △ to stand for an unknown number.

❑ Use simple multiplication to solve simple word problems involving numbers in 'real life'.

Resources
none

Teaching support

Misconceptions
When children are faced with word problems to solve they often default to adding the numbers in the question. Encourage them to draw a simple sketch of each problem to ensure they think fully about the situation. Ask children to write answers for question 3 as a number sentence to show their working.

The key idea is that children should practise multiplication facts for 2, 5 and 10.

Children should have begun to develop their understanding of multiplication and to recognise from arranging arrays that multiplication can be done in any order.

▪ Practise counting up in 2s. Ask questions such as *Five lots of 2 is …?* and relate it to a practical context: *Five children each have two ears. How many ears altogether?*

▪ Introduce the words 'twice' and 'times'. Ask further oral questions related to the two-times table e.g. *Twice 2, 10 times 2, …*

▪ Count up in 10s and ask related questions: *Twice ten, 4 groups of 10, 9 times 10 …*

▪ Revise the use of the multiplication sign to represent these facts, e.g. $4 \times 10 = 40$, $8 \times 2 = 16$, etc. Provide several examples of missing number questions, where the missing number is represented by a box, e.g. $5 \times \square = 50$.

Things to say and ask

❑ *What does 4×5 mean?*
❑ *How do we say it? How many is four lots of five?*
❑ *How could we work this out?*

Answers
1 a 10 **b** 14 **c** 6 **d** 2 **e** 80 **f** 9
2 a 20 **b** 5 **c** 4 **d** 30 **e** 9 **f** any pair of factors of 16
3 a 30 **b** $5 \times 4 = 20$ **c** $2 \times 6 = 12$ **d** $7 \times 2 = 14$ **e** $8 \times 10 = 80$
  f own word problem

Doubles and halves

Activity Sheet 58

Objectives

- ❏ Know and use halving as the inverse of doubling.
- ❏ Know by heart doubles of all numbers to 10 and corresponding halves.

Vocabulary

double, half, halve, twice, times as

Resources

about 20 cubes (per group)

0–9 dice (per pair)

about 20 counters (per pair)

Teaching support

The key idea is that children should become confident at doubling and halving small numbers. This will later be a useful strategy for performing mental calculations with larger numbers.

Children should already be familiar with the terms 'double' and 'half' and should know by heart doubles to five.

- Begin by revising the meaning of the word 'double'. Hold several cubes in your hand. *I have …. cubes in my hand. If I double the number of cubes I have, what does this mean?* Collect the same number of cubes and hold them in your other hand. *Double means that I have twice or two times as many.* Ask children to say how many cubes you have. *How many is that altogether?* Call out a number to 5 and ask children to say the double.

- Similarly revise the word 'half'. Take an even number of cubes and place them in your lap. *I have 8 cubes. To find half of 8 I need to split them into two sets.* Stress that the sets must be the same size. Take some in one hand and some in the other. *I have 4 in this hand and the same number in this hand. So half of 8 is 4.* Again call out even numbers to 10 and ask children to say half.

- Some children may find cubes useful when halving a number such as 16 or 18, e.g. splitting 16 into two sets the same size.

- Children should notice that when a number is halved and then doubled it returns to the same number; in other words halving is the inverse of doubling and vice versa.

- Discuss children's answers to question 2, and encourage them to notice that all the answers are even numbers. *Are all doubles of numbers to 10 even numbers?*

Things to say and ask

- ❏ *What is double six? Which number is twice as big as eight?*
- ❏ *How did you double this number?*
- ❏ *What do you notice about all your answers to the double questions? (even)*
- ❏ *What would happen if you halved your answer?*
- ❏ *What happens if we halve eight, then double it?*
- ❏ *What is half of twelve? How many is twelve split into two groups?*
- ❏ *For the game: What is double zero?*

Answers

1	**a**	6	**b**	8	**c**	10		
2	**b**	8	**c**	12	**d**	16		
3	**b**	4	**c**	3	**d**	6	**e**	8
4	**a**	5		10				
	b	7		14				

Division as sharing

Activity Sheet 59

Objectives

Vocabulary

share equally, between, one each, two each …, divide, divided by, equal groups of

- ❑ Begin to understand division as sharing.
- ❑ Use and begin to read the related vocabulary.
- ❑ Use the ÷ and = signs.

Resources
about 20 cubes (per child)

Teaching support

The key idea is that children should begin to understand division as sharing equally.

Children should be confident with simple multiplication and be familiar with doubling and halving numbers up to 20.

- Begin by asking 3 children to the front. Give each child 2 cubes. *Each of these children has 2 cubes. How many is this altogether?* Give them each an extra cube. *Each of these children has 3 cubes. How many is this altogether?* Take all the cubes from the children but ask them to remain at the front. Now put 12 cubes on the table. *If I share 12 cubes out so that each child has the same number, how many will they get each?* Invite a child to come to the front and share out the cubes between the 3 children so that each has 4.

- Show children how to record this. Introduce the division sign (÷) as meaning 'shared equally between' or 'divided by'. Write 12 ÷ 3 = on the board. Ask the children to read this aloud as *twelve shared equally between three is four.*

- Write 15 ÷ 3 = on the board. *What does this mean? How would we say this?* Ask children to say 'Fifteen shared equally between three' and to work out the answer using cubes.

- Emphasise the importance of each group being equal and use the terms 'share equally' and 'divided by'.

Things to say and ask

- ❑ *If we had 20 cubes, how could we share them equally into two groups, four groups, five and ten groups?*
- ❑ *How did you work this out? Did you use cubes? Did you know a number fact that helped you?*
- ❑ *How many different ways do you think that we could share 12 cubes equally?*
- ❑ *How could we write this as a number sentence?*

Answers

1 b 6	c 5	d 4	e 5	f 5	
2 a 6	b 3	c 2			
3 b 4	c 6	d 4	e 6	f 6	

Division as grouping

Activity Sheet 60

Objectives

❏ Begin to understand division as grouping (repeated subtraction).

❏ Use and begin to read the related vocabulary.

❏ Use the ÷ and = signs.

Vocabulary

groups, equal groups of

Resources
20 cubes (per child)

Teaching support

Children should have had some experience of multiplication, doubling and halving numbers. They should be confident with the division sign as meaning 'shared equally between'.

Misconceptions

Children can become confused with the two types of division, equal sharing and equal grouping. It is important not to discuss all practical work in terms of division as sharing and then, when introducing the formal division sign, e.g. 8 ÷ 2, to explain this as *how many twos in eight?* Ensure that, once children are confident with sharing, grouping is introduced practically.

◼ Explain that today you are going to look at another way of understanding the ÷ sign.

◼ Show the children 8 cubes. Explain you are going to split them into groups of 2. Take 2 cubes to form the first group. *I've made one group of two.* Take another 2 cubes. *Now I have two groups of two.* Repeat for the final 2 groups. *If I have eight cubes I can make four groups of two cubes.*

◼ Show how to record this as 8 ÷ 2 = 4

◼ Repeat for 6 cubes split into 3 groups: *How many groups of three are there in six?*

◼ Repeat for 15 cubes split into 3 groups. Focus on forming one group at a time and separating it (taking it away) from the total number.

Things to say and ask

❏ *How did you work this out? Did you use cubes? Did you know a number fact?*
❏ *If we had 20 cubes, how can we group them equally?*
❏ *How many different ways do you think that we could group 12 cubes equally?*
❏ *How could we write this as a number sentence?*

Answers

1	a	6	b	4	c	3	d	2
2	a	10	b	5	c	4	d	2

3 5
   2
   1

4 9
   6
   3

Division problems

Activity Sheet 61

Vocabulary

share equally, equal groups of, divide, divided by

❑ Derive quickly division facts for the 2 and 10 times tables.

❑ Recognise the use of a symbol such as ❑ or Δ to stand for an unknown number.

❑ Solve simple word problems involving numbers in 'real life'.

Resources
a set of even number cards from 2 to 20 and a ÷2 card (per pair)

The key idea is that children should use their knowledge of the 2 and 10 times tables to help them solve division puzzles and problems.

Children should have practised the 2 and 10 times tables. They should also have begun to understand division as sharing and as grouping and be familiar with the ÷ sign.

▪ Ask children to count on in twos from zero. At a certain point call out 'Stop!', e.g. *2, 4, 6, 8, Stop!* Write the last number spoken onto the board, e.g. 8. *How many twos have we counted to reach 8?* Show this as a division fact on the board, e.g. 8 ÷ 2 = 4. Ask oral questions related to this fact, e.g. *'How many groups of two in eight?* Repeat the counting process for other facts, beginning the count from zero each time and calling 'Stop!', e.g. *2, 4, 6, 8, 10, 12, 14 Stop!* Show the division fact for each, e.g. 14 ÷ 2 = 7. Remind children of the terms 'divided by' and division.

▪ Repeat for division facts for 10.

▪ Provide several examples of missing number questions, where the missing number is represented by a box or other shape, e.g. 8 ÷ ☐ = 4 or ☐ ÷ 10 = 5

❑ *How many twos have we counted to reach 8?*
❑ *How many twos in eight?*
❑ *What is 80 divided by 10?*

Answers
1 **a** 6   **b** 2   **c** 70   **d** 6   **e** 10   **f** 20
2 The most likely answers are 12 ÷ 2 = 6 and 60 ÷ 10 = 6, but others are possible.
3 **a** 9   **b** 6   **c** 3   **d** 2

Halves and doubles

Objectives

Vocabulary

double, halve, divide

❑ Derive quickly: doubles of multiples of 5 to 50; halves of multiples of 10 to 100.

❑ Use simple division to solve simple word problems involving numbers in money using one step.

Resources
none

Teaching support

The key idea is that children should extend the range of numbers they can double and halve with confidence. This will later be a useful strategy for performing mental calculations with larger numbers. Children should already be familiar with doubling and halving numbers to 10.

▪ Introduce a strategy for doubling multiples of 5, e.g. when doubling a 2-digit number split the number into tens and units and double each part separately and combine the answers e.g.

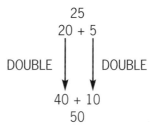

25
20 + 5

DOUBLE ↓   ↓ DOUBLE

40 + 10
50

▪ Encourage children to notice that if the tens digit in the number is odd, then half of the number will end in 5, e.g. half of 30 is 15. Where the tens digit is even, the halved number will end in 0.

Things to say and ask

❑ *What is double fifteen? How many is twice fifty?*
❑ *How did you double this number?*
❑ *What would happen if you halved your answer?*
❑ *What happens if we halve the number first and then double the answer?*
❑ *If we halve this number will the answer end in 5 or 0?*

Answers

1

55	10	60	80	15
38	50	34	14	5
65	70	40	12	99
42	90	16	52	85
24	30	20	100	36

Capital E should be coloured.

2 **a** 5p **b** 15p **c** 20p **d** 10p **e** 30p
f 25p **g** 40p **h** 35p **i** 45p **j** 50p

Estimating and measuring lengths

Activity Sheet 63

Objectives

Vocabulary

measure, compare, estimate, nearly, roughly, about, close to, just over, just under, length, width, height, depth, long, short, tall, high, far, further, furthest, metre, centimetre, ruler, metre stick, geostrip

❑ Use and begin to read the vocabulary related to length.

❑ Estimate, measure and compare lengths using standard units (m, cm).

❑ Suggest suitable units and equipment for such measurements.

Resources
metre stick (per pair)

ruler (per pair)

cm interlocking cubes (per group)

set of objects to measure: new pencils, dominoes, playing cards, geostrip (per pair)

key vocabulary displayed in the classroom (include comparative words such as longer, longest …)

Teaching support

Misconceptions

The abbreviations 'm' and 'cm' do not have an additional 's' in the plural form, for example, 10 cm is read as 10 centimetres and 2 metres is recorded as 2 m.

In question 2, some children may leave spaces between objects when finding the number in 1 metre.

The key idea is that the metre and the centimetre are standard units of length, and that 1 metre is the same length as 100 centimetres.

Children should have had experience of making direct comparisons of lengths, of making estimates and of measuring to the nearest metre using a metre stick. They should also have had experience of measuring with a ruler.

◼ Revise key vocabulary and introduce children to any new words such as 'further' and 'furthest'.

◼ Give pairs of children metre sticks and ask them to find objects, distances or measurements on their bodies that are 'shorter than 1 metre', 'about 1 metre' and 'longer than 1 metre'. Discuss measurements that are 'shorter than 1 metre' and bring out the need for a smaller standard unit.

◼ Introduce the word 'centimetre' and the abbreviations 'm' and 'cm'.

◼ Ask children to make rods of cm cubes to match the length of a small object, e.g. a pencil or a lunch box.

◼ Children use their rods of cubes to find the depths of the fish in question 1.

◼ If materials are limited, provide one set of objects and ask each pair to begin question 2 at a different starting point, e.g. the first pair starts with pencils, the second with dominoes, etc.

Things to say and ask

❑ *Suppose you had only one new pencil. How could you find how many make one metre?*

❑ *Why should you use words such as 'just over', 'nearly' or 'about' when you work out the number of objects in one metre?*

❑ *What would you use to measure the width of your handspan? The length of the board?*

Answers
1 b 5 cm   **c** 2 cm   **d** 6 cm   **e** 4 cm   **f** 1 cm

2 (Child's own answers.)

Measuring lengths

Activity Sheet 64

Vocabulary

measuring scale, length, width, height, depth, metre, centimetre, ruler, metre stick, tape measure

❑ Read a simple scale to the nearest labelled division, including using a ruler to draw and measure lines to the nearest centimetre, recording estimates and measurements as '3 and a bit metres long' or 'about 8 centimetres'.

Resources

cm interlocking cubes (per group)

rulers: dead-end and waste-end (see Misconceptions) (per child)

metre sticks and measuring tapes calibrated in cm (per group)

Misconceptions

Errors occur when children do not align the start of the edge or line to be measured with zero (waste-end ruler, on which the scale starts slightly in from the edge) or with the left-hand edge (dead-end ruler, on which the scale starts at the edge).

The key idea is that when measuring a length, children should begin at the zero, or if there is no zero marked on the ruler, at the left-hand end.

Children should have experience of counting in 10s, and of multiples of 10. They should also be able to round numbers to the nearest 10.

Help children to develop skills in using a ruler (to measure and draw lines) and in using a metre stick and tape measure in the following ways:

◻ Ask children to make rods of different lengths out of cm cubes and to measure them with a ruler. They should discover that the number of cubes in a rod matches the numeral it reaches on the ruler.

◻ Children could draw lines of different lengths, swap papers and check their partner's work.

◻ Ask children to measure and compare the lengths of small objects on their desk, e.g. a pencil.

◻ Give children practice in measuring heights, widths, distances, etc. to the nearest 10 cm on a metre stick or measuring tape.

❑ *How far from the floor is the big dog's collar? The end of the smallest dog's ears?*
❑ *Draw two zig-zag lines, up to 30 cm long, on the other side of your sheet. Swap with a partner and measure each other's lines.*

Answers

1   a   pencil 6 cm, crayon 4 cm, The pencil is 2 cm longer than the crayon.
    b   frog 6 cm, mouse 4 cm, The mouse is 2 cm shorter than the frog.
2   a   30 cm   b   60 cm   c   40 cm
3   a   14 cm   b   18 cm

Estimating and measuring mass

Activity Sheet 65

Objectives

Vocabulary

measure, compare, guess, estimate, nearly, roughly, about, close to, about the same as, just over, just under, weight, weighs, balances, heavy, light, kilogram, half-kilogram, gram, balance, scales

- ❑ Use and begin to read the vocabulary related to mass.
- ❑ Estimate, measure and compare mass using standard units (kg).
- ❑ Suggest suitable units and equipment for such measurements.

Resources

balance scales (per group and pair)

1 kg weights (per group)

small objects such as marbles, cubes, dominoes (per group)

objects such as grocery items for weighing (per group)

tea cup (per pair)

sand, rice and pasta (per pair)

key vocabulary displayed in the classroom (include comparative words such as heavier, heaviest …)

Teaching support

Misconceptions

Children should realise that the weight of an object is not directly related to its size.

The key idea is that the kilogram is the standard unit of mass.

Children should have experience of comparing weights by 'hand weighing' and saying which is lighter and which is heavier.

- ■ Introduce the need for a standard unit of mass by weighing an object such as a tub of yoghurt using a range of uniform non-standard units, e.g. marbles or cubes.
- ■ Help children refine their weighing skills. Estimate and compare by 'hand weighing' an object and a 1 kilogram weight. *Which is heavier/lighter? Or do they both feel about the same weight?*
- ■ Referring to the balance scales and the 1 kg weight, discuss with children how these provide a more accurate means of weighing objects or grocery items in a range of sizes. Introduce children to the abbreviated 'kg'. Show that a 1 kg weight balances a 1 kg bag of sugar, flour, rice or pasta.
- ■ In pairs, ask children to estimate and measure items, recording 'lighter than 1 kg', 'about 1 kg', 'heavier than 1 kg'.
- ■ Establish the need for a standard unit smaller than 1 kg and explain that 1 kilogram is the same as 1000 grams. A half-kilogram is 500 grams.

Things to say and ask

- ❑ *Check that the rice is level with the top of the cup.*
- ❑ *If you tap the side of the cup, will it hold more pasta?*

Answers

1 Match each object to the correct label.

lighter than 1kg   heavier than 1kg

2 and **3** Child's own answers.

Weighing in kilograms

Activity Sheet 66

Objective

Vocabulary

measuring scale, nearly, just over, just under, about, about the same as, kilogram, half-kilogram, scales, weight

❏ Read a simple scale to the nearest labelled division, recording estimates and measurements as 'nearly 3 kilograms heavy'.

Resources
kitchen and bathroom compression scales with dials calibrated in kg (per group)

5 objects or parcels weighing between 1 kg and 5 kg (per group)

1 kg weight (per group)

Teaching support

Misconceptions
Children may not realise that approximations such as 'nearly 3 kilograms' are acceptable answers.

The key idea is that we measure mass in kilograms.

Children need to be able to read the scale on a ruler.

◻ Before the lesson, recalibrate the kitchen scales by sticking on labels to show only intervals of 1 kg.

◻ Discuss and compare kitchen and bathroom scales by placing a 1 kg weight on both scales. *On the kitchen scales the hand moves round the dial to 1 kg. On the bathroom scales the hand stays in the centre while the dial turns to the 1 kg mark.*

◻ Support children in developing skills in reading a simple scale to the nearest kilogram.

◻ Children estimate and use both scales to measure a range of objects or parcels.

◻ Emphasise the need to use the language 'nearly/about/just over/just under 3 kg' when recording weights.

Things to say and ask

❏ *Do you think you could lift something as heavy as the sheep in question 2a?*
❏ *About how many kilograms do you weigh?*
❏ *What is the total weight of all the puppies in questions 1a and 1b?*

Answers
1	a	2 kg	b	3 kg	c	4 kg						
2	a	8 kg	b	6 kg	c	11 kg	d	9 kg	e	14 kg	f	12 kg
3	b, a, d, c, e											

Estimating and measuring capacity

Activity Sheet 67

Vocabulary

capacity, full, empty, holds, contains, litre, half-litre, millilitre, container, guess, estimate, measure, compare, measuring scale, about the same as, close to, just over, just under

❑ Use and begin to read the vocabulary related to capacity.

❑ Estimate, measure and compare capacities using standard units (litre).

❑ Suggest suitable units and equipment for such measurements.

Resources
4 clear plastic bottles of different sizes and shapes labelled W, X, Y and Z

uniform non-standard measures, e.g. cups, mugs, pots

3 differently-shaped 1 litre containers

1 litre measuring jug (per pair)

funnel (per pair)

water (per pair)

3 small containers labelled A, B and C, e.g. cup, mug, yoghurt pot (per pair)

coloured pencils (per child)

key vocabulary displayed in the classroom

Teaching support

Misconceptions
Some children may have difficulty with the concept of conservation of capacity. This will develop over time through practical experiences.

The key idea is that the litre is the standard unit of capacity.

Children should be able to compare directly two capacities and say which container holds more and which holds less.

■ Show the bottles labelled W, X, Y and Z. To help children develop the concept of conservation of capacity, pour a cupful of water into each bottle. Compare the levels and establish that the shape of the bottle does not affect the amount of water in it.

■ Introduce the need for a standard unit of capacity. Fill one container with water measured using a range of uniform non-standard units, e.g. first using cups, then mugs, then pots.

■ Display the 1 litre containers and measuring jug. Show that all the containers have a capacity of approximately 1 litre by filling the measuring jug to the 1 litre mark and pouring it, in turn, into the other containers. Introduce the abbreviation l.

■ Remind children of the techniques of pouring and emptying liquids into and from containers.

■ Discuss why containers are rarely filled to the brim.

■ Establish the need for a standard unit smaller than 1 litre and explain that 1 litre is the same as 1000 millilitres. A half-litre is 500 millilitres.

Things to say and ask

❑ *Which holds more water, a cup or a yoghurt pot? How do you know?*
❑ *About how many cupfuls/mugfuls are the same as half a litre?*

Answers
1 and **2** Child's own answers.

Measuring litres in jugs and jars

Activity Sheet 68

Objective

Vocabulary

capacity, full, empty, holds, contains, litre, half-litre, container, guess, estimate, measure, compare, measuring scale, about, least, most, close to, just over, just under

❑ Read a simple scale to the nearest labelled division, recording estimates and measurements.

Resources

3 containers: less than 1 litre, about 1 litre, more than 1 litre (per group)

1 litre measuring jug (per group)

water (per group)

3 hoops labelled 'holds less than 1 litre', 'holds about 1 litre', 'holds more than 1 litre' (per group)

blue coloured pencil (per child)

Teaching support

Misconceptions

Check that children read the scales and interpret the approximation terms correctly.

The key idea is that capacity is the amount of space in a hollow container.

Children should be able to read a scale on a ruler or on a decimetre-marked metre stick to the nearest labelled division.

▪ Place the three containers in front of the group. Ask children to put the containers in order from 'holds least' to 'holds most'.

▪ Ask the group to select the container they estimate will hold about 1 litre. Set children to use water and a 1 litre measuring jug to check the capacities. Remind them to read the scale at eye level.

▪ Encourage children to work co-operatively as they investigate the capacities of the remaining two containers. Ask children to place the containers in the appropriate labelled hoop.

Things to say and ask

❑ For question 2b: *You pour out 30 litres. About how many litres are left in the jar?*

❑ For question 2f: *Imagine you pour more water into the jar to double the amount. How many litres do you pour in? Now you fill it to the 40 litre mark. How many litres do you add?*

Answers

1 Levels coloured up to the following marks:

    a 4l   **b** 7l   **c** 6l   **d** 9l

2 **a** 20   **b** 40   **c** 30   **d** 50   **e** 60   **f** 10

3 1 litre of water weighs 1 kg

Estimating and measuring time

Activity Sheet 69

Objectives

Vocabulary

days of the week: Monday, Tuesday, …, day, week, fortnight, night, yesterday, today, tomorrow, before, after, hour, minute, second, how long will it take to? timer

❑ Use and begin to read the vocabulary related to time.

❑ Use units of time and know the relationships between them (second, minute, hour, day, week).

❑ Suggest suitable units to estimate or measure time.

Resources
1-minute and 2-minute timers (per pair)

plastic square (per pair)

pegboard and pegs (per pair)

cm cubes (per pair)

2 straws (per pair)

about 20 counters (per pair)

paper plate (per pair)

Teaching support

Misconceptions
Some children relate time to base 10 instead of base 60 and make errors such as 100 seconds = 1 minute, 100 minutes = 1 hour.

The key idea is to develop an understanding of the units of time and the relationship between them, as well as to begin to estimate time.

Children should know in order the days of the week, be able to order familar events and talk about how often events occur using appropriate vocabulary.

▪ Recall the order of the days of the week. Introduce 'fortnight' as a period of 14 days.

▪ Discuss units of time shorter than 1 day: how clocks or watches show hours, minutes and seconds. Ensure children understand the abbreviations for hours (hr), minutes (min) and seconds (sec).

▪ Practise measuring the duration of 30 seconds by counting and clapping: *one*, clap, clap; *two*, clap, clap; *three*, clap, clap… or saying: *one Mississippi, two Mississippi….*

▪ Practise estimating a minute, e.g. children sit down when they think a minute has passed.

▪ Discuss the relationships between seconds, minutes and hours and ask which units children would use to measure given time durations.

Things to say and ask

❑ *Which unit of time is the same as two weeks?*
❑ *Which unit would you use to measure a yawn? The time you spend in school?*
❑ *What takes about ten seconds? One minute? Half an hour? One hour?*
❑ *In one minute you wrote your name twenty times. How many times can you write it in thirty seconds? In two minutes?*

Answers

1

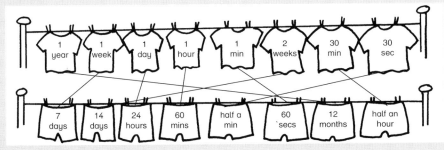

2 and **3** Child's own answers.

Month by month

Objectives

☐ Order familiar events in time.

☐ Order the months of the year.

Vocabulary

months of the year:
January, February, …,
month, year, before, after,
next, last, birthday,
holiday

Resources

set of cards: 12 ordinal numbers (1st, 2nd, … 12th)

set of cards: 12 months of the year

set of cards: spring, summer, autumn, winter

1–6 dice (per pair)

dice labelled O, B, O, B, O, B (per pair)

coloured pencils (per pair)

Teaching support

Misconceptions

Some events have the same date every year, e.g. birthdays, Christmas; some have different dates, e.g. Divali, Hanukkah, Easter.

The key idea is to begin to recognise special events in the year and to develop an understanding of the cycle of the months of the year.

Children should have had an opportunity to look at and discuss calendars.

▣ Place the ordinal cards in sequence. Hand out the month cards and check that children can read their card(s). Beginning with January, ask children to put the month cards in order, matching them with the ordinal cards.

▣ Ask questions such as: *How many months come before May? After September? What is the sixth month of the year? Which month comes before/after December? Which months come between the seventh month and the tenth month? When is your birthday?*

▣ Show the children the seasons cards. Ask questions such as: *Which are the months of winter? Of spring? Which season is it in August? In May?*

▣ Before photocopying the Activity Sheet, choose one more 'special' day and write it in question 1.

Things to say and ask

☐ *What do we celebrate in the eleventh month of the year? In which month/season do we have Guy Fawkes Day?*

Answers

1

Reading the time

Objective

❑ Read the time to the hour, half-hour or quarter-hour on an analogue clock and a 12-hour digital clock, and understand the notation 7:30.

Vocabulary

o'clock, half past, quarter to, quarter past, digital/ analogue clock/watch

Resources
geared analogue clock (per group)
digital clock (per group)

Teaching support

Misconceptions
Check that the hour hand is positioned correctly, e.g. at 2:30 the hour hand is halfway between 2 and 3; at 2:15/2:45 it is one/three quarters of the way between 2 and 3.

The key idea is for children to read times and to link analogue and digital time displays. Reading the digital displays '7:30' as 'half past seven' and '7:15' as 'quarter past seven' will help children to make this link.

Children should have experience of setting analogue clocks to hour and half-hour times.

▪ Set the analogue and digital clocks to display 9 o'clock and 9:00. Invite suggestions as to where children have seen similar clock faces. Elicit that both show the same time.

▪ Give children practice in setting both types of clock face to hour and half-hour times.

▪ Show the minute hand turning from 9 o'clock to quarter past 9. Explain that the minute hand has moved one quarter of the way round the clock face so the clock is showing quarter past 9.

▪ Display the digital time of 9:15. Read aloud as *quarter past nine* and *fifteen minutes past nine*.

▪ Set the digital time 9:45. Explain that 9:45 shows 3 lots of 15 minutes and is read as *quarter to ten* or *fifteen minutes to ten*. Ask: *Who can set the analogue clock to quarter to ten?*

▪ Discuss the positioning of the hour hand at the quarter- and half-hours. Give the children practice in setting both types of clock face to quarter past/quarter to times.

Things to say and ask

❑ *How far round the dial does the minute hand turn from 12 to 3? How far does it turn from 9 to 12?*

❑ *If there are 60 minutes in one hour, how many minutes are in half an hour? In quarter of an hour?*

Answers

1	**a**	half past 11	**b**	quarter to 4	**c**	quarter past 6	**d** half past 12
	e	quarter past 9	**f**	quarter to 3			
2	**a**	4:45	**b**	6:15	**c**	7:00	**d** 8:45
3	**a**	3:15	**b**	4:45			

Measuring length problems

Activity Sheet 72

Objectives

Vocabulary

measure, compare, guess, estimate, length, width, height, depth, far, further, furthest, metre, centimetre, ruler

❏ Use mental addition and subtraction, simple multiplication and division, to solve simple word problems involving numbers in measures, using one or two steps.

❏ Explain how the problem was solved.

❏ Choose and use appropriate operations and efficient calculation strategies to solve problems.

Resources

3 pieces of ribbon (paper strips) cut to lengths of 15 cm, 20 cm and 25 cm (per group)

3 blank sticky labels (per group)

ruler (per group)

Teaching support

The key idea is that in solving a problem we need to: read the problem carefully, identify the key information, choose the appropriate operation(s), use efficient calculation strategies and find the answer to the problem.

Children need to be able to use a ruler to measure to the nearest centimetre.

▪ Set up problem-solving situations to make children aware of the mathematics they use to solve problems, and to encourage reflection and discussion of the strategies used, e.g. ask a child to measure and label the three pieces of ribbon (15 cm, 20 cm, 25 cm). *Suppose I lost my ruler. How could I use the ribbons to measure 5 cm?* (difference between 20 cm and 15 cm) *To measure 10 cm?* (half of 20 cm) *To measure 40 cm?* (15 cm + 25 cm or double 20 cm)

▪ Pose the problem: *A baker uses 30 cm of ribbon to go round a birthday cake. How much ribbon will she need for two cakes? For four cakes?*

▪ Ask children in pairs to make up a problem which uses the ribbon lengths in a meaningful context, e.g. a ribbon on a birthday cake or card, a sports medal, a bow, etc.

Things to say and ask

❏ *Who found a different way?*
❏ *Can you tell us how you solved the problem?*
❏ *Who found a quick way to add 15 to 25?*
❏ *What did you do?*

Answers

1 $12 + 9 = 21$ m	**2** $25 + 5 = 30$ cm	**3** $70 - 14 = 56$ cm
4 $8 - 3 = 5$ m	**5** $80 \div 2 = 40$ cm	**6** 26 m

83

Measuring mass problems

Activity Sheet 73

Objectives

Vocabulary

heavier/lighter, kilogram, half-kilogram, balance, scales, weight

❏ Use mental addition and subtraction, simple multiplication and division, to solve simple word problems involving numbers in measures, using one or two steps.

❏ Explain how the problem was solved.

Resources
3 cards labelled 'Jock 4 kg', 'Maggie 6 kg' and 'Hamish 8 kg' (per group)

Teaching support

The key idea is to focus on the problem-solving steps: read the problem carefully and identify the key information; choose the appropriate operation(s); use efficient calculation strategies; find the answer to the problem.

Children need to have an understanding of doubles and near doubles.

▪ Display the labels. Explain that three Scottie dogs were taken to the vet's for a check-up and the labels show their weights. Pose questions to compare weights and stimulate reasoning, such as:
How many kilograms heavier/lighter is Maggie than Jock? Than Hamish?
Two dogs stand on the scales. Their total weight is 12/14 kilograms. Can you name the dogs?
What can you tell me about the weights of Jock and Hamish?
A bag of 'Dog-e-bits' weighs three kilograms. It lasts Maggie for two weeks. How much 'Dog-e-bits' will she eat in four weeks? In eight weeks?
Which of the three dogs is the puppy? Why do you think that?

▪ Conclude by asking the children to pose some questions of their own.

Things to say and ask

❏ *How much heavier is the puppy than the rabbit? Than the guinea pig? Than the kitten?*
❏ *Who can think of a quick way to find the total weight of four kittens? Of six kittens?*

Answers

1

2 a 12 kg **b** 7 kg **c** A, B and D
3 a 15 kg **b** 14 kg **c** 16 kg
4 puppy

Measuring capacity problems

Activity Sheet 74

Objectives

Vocabulary

capacity, full, empty, holds, contains, litre, container, about

❏ Use mental addition and subtraction, simple multiplication and division, to solve simple word problems involving numbers in measures, using one or two steps.

❏ Explain how the problem was solved.

❏ Choose and use appropriate operations and efficient calculation strategies to solve problems.

Resources
range of 1 litre and 2 litre commercial containers and cartons (per group)

Teaching support

Misconceptions
If children have difficulty in identifying the calculation needed, ask them to express the problem in their own words. *What do you know? What have you to find out?*

The key idea is to focus on the problem-solving steps: read the problem carefully and identify the key information; choose the appropriate operation(s); use efficient calculation strategies; find the answer to the problem.

Children need to have a sound knowledge of doubles.

▪ Display the containers and cartons. Ask questions which encourage reasoning and explanations of methods used, such as:
Which containers together make up four litres? Five litres? Ten litres?
I have a ten litre basin. I pour in the contents of these containers (three 2 litres and one 1 litre). Which containers will I use to fill the basin? Is there another way I can do it?
How many different ways can I make six litres with these cartons?
You can make five cups of coffee from a one litre kettle. How many cups of coffee can you make with a two/three/four litre kettle?

Things to say and ask

❏ *Can you see a pattern in Ginger's answers? Can you describe the pattern?*
❏ *What if Suki wants to measure out ten litres of orange juice? How many different ways can she do it?*

Answers
1 6 litres, 6 jugs
2 **a** 8   **b** 12   **c** 16   **d** 5
3 (2 + 2 + 1) = 5 l, (2 + 1 + 1 + 1) = 5 l, (1 + 1 + 1 + 1 + 1) = 5 l
4 five 2 l cartons

Time puzzles

Activity Sheet 75

Objectives

Vocabulary

minute, hour, o'clock, half past, quarter to/past, 15 minutes to/past, before, after, digital/analogue clock/watch

❏ Solve mathematical problems or puzzles.

❏ Explain how the problem was solved.

Resources
calendar (per group)
analogue and digital clock faces (per group)

Misconceptions

Using an analogue clock face can help children who have difficulty in bridging through 12, e.g. 2 hours after 11:15 (or quarter past 11) is 1:15 (or quarter past 1).

The key idea is to pose problems and puzzles that encourage children to reflect, discuss and explain their methods and strategies.

Children need a sound understanding of reading the time to the hour, half hour and quarter hour on an analogue or digital clock, and of the notation 7:30. They need to be familiar with the layout of a calendar.

- Choose a month in which more than one child has a birthday. Circle the dates on the calendar. Ask questions which involve identifying dates and days of the week, such as:
  Amy's birthday is the first Tuesday of July. What date is that?
  Derek's birthday is a fortnight later. How many days later? What is the day and date of his birthday?
  Who has a birthday between the second and third Sundays of the month?

- Write on the board: 8:15, 10:30, 1:45. Ask children to set the analogue and digital clock faces to times that are 1 hour, 1 hour 30 minutes and 2 hours later or earlier. Discuss strategies for bridging through 12.

- *The 8:15 flight to Majorca is delayed by 1 hour 30 minutes. What is the new take-off time? How did you work it out?*

Answers

1 **b** 26 July   **c** 20 July   **d** 22 July
2 quarter past 11, 3:45, half past 1, 12:15
3 1:30   1:45   10:45   3:45   4:15   4:30   5:30

Measuring heights

Activity Sheet 76

Vocabulary

explain your method, length, height, high, higher, highest, low, lower, lowest, far, further, furthest, metre

- Repeat addition in a different order.

- Check with an equivalent calculation.

- Use mental addition and subtraction, simple multiplication and division, to solve simple word problems involving numbers in measures, using one or two steps.

- Explain how the problem was solved.

Resources
4 cards labelled 15 m, 20 m, 23 m and 24 m

The key idea is that there may be several ways of checking whether an answer is correct.

Children should have a sound knowledge of adding or subtracting a pair of numbers to at least 20 and be able to bridge through 10.

- Show the cards labelled 23 m and 24 m. Discuss how separating numbers into tens and units makes addition problems easier to solve, e.g. 23 + 24 = 20 + 20 + 3 + 4 = 40 + 7 = 47. Discuss ways to check the addition. Repeat for other lengths.
- Encourage children to work out answers to questions 1 and 2 on the Activity Sheet in their heads. Some children may need help in interpreting the problems in question 2.
- Remind children that there are various ways of finding answers for question 3, such as putting the larger number first, using doubles or near doubles, and so on.

Things to say and ask

- *What should these lengths add up to?*
- *Tell me a good way of checking whether the answer is correct. Is there another way to work it out?*
- *Can you explain your method? Would it work with different numbers?*

Answers

1 a 4 m   b 6 m   c 10 m   d 15 m
2 a 6   b 4, 5   c Acorn   d Pipkin
3 19 m + 21 m = 40 m   19 m + 24 m = 43 m
   21 m + 24 m = 45 m   21 m + 25 m = 46 m   24 m + 25 m = 49 m

Weight puzzles

Activity Sheet 77

Objectives

Vocabulary

compare, weigh, weight, kilogram

- Choose and use appropriate operations and efficient calculation strategies (e.g. mental, mental with jottings) to solve problems.
- Use mental addition and subtraction, simple multiplication and division, to solve simple word problems involving numbers in measures, using one or two steps.
- Explain how the problem was solved.
- Solve mathematical problems or puzzles.

Resources
5 boxes labelled 8 kg, 9 kg, 11 kg, 14 kg, 15 kg
supply of cards labelled 1 kg, 2 kg, 5 kg, 10 kg

Teaching support

Misconceptions

If children have difficulty in identifying the calculation needed, ask them to pose the problem in their own words and to select the relevant information.

The key idea is to look for an efficient way to work out the answer to a problem or puzzle.

Children should have a sound understanding of doubles and near doubles.

▪ Show the boxes and cards and encourage the children to visualise the practical weighing process for the following problem:

'In the village Post Office there is a large two-pan balance and a supply of 1 kg, 2 kg, 5 kg and 10 kg weights. Sandy the postmaster is checking the weight of these five parcels.'

Which parcels can he balance with only two weights? Which weights are they?

Which parcels can he balance with only three weights? Which weights did he use?

Sandy is a clever postmaster. He can check the weight of the 9 kg parcel using only two weights, 10 kg and 1 kg. Who can work out how he did it? Can you show us?
(9 kg parcel + 1 kg balances 10 kg)

Who can think of a clever way to check the weight of the 14 kg parcel?

Things to say and ask

❑ For question 2: *How can you check your answers?*
❑ For question 3: *How might you split up 15 kg to make the calculation easier?*

Answers

1 11 kg + 15 kg = 26 kg; 11 kg + 16 kg = 27 kg; 11 kg + 19 kg = 30 kg;
15 kg + 16 kg = 31 kg; 15 kg + 19 kg = 34 kg; 16 kg + 19 kg = 35 kg

2 a 16 kg – 11 kg = 5 kg   **b** 19 kg – 15 kg = 4 kg

3 45 kg

4 5 kg

Picture the shape

Activity Sheet 78

Objectives

Vocabulary

name, circle, triangle, square, rectangle, pentagon, hexagon, octagon, straight, corner, side

❑ Use the mathematical names for common 2-D shapes, including the pentagon, hexagon, octagon.

❑ Sort shapes and describe some of their features, such as the number of sides and corners, symmetry.

❑ Make and describe shapes, pictures and patterns.

Resources

pinboard (per child)

elastic band (per child)

2 large paper triangles

2 large paper squares

set of 2-D shapes (per group)

scissors

1–6 dice (per group)

approx. 80 straws or matchsticks (per group)

Teaching support

Misconceptions

Check that children can name an irregular shape correctly, e.g. a chevron has 6 sides and is a hexagon.

The key idea is that a flat shape with 5 straight sides is a pentagon, with 6 straight sides is a hexagon and with 8 straight sides is an octagon.

Children should already be able to identify a circle, triangle, square and rectangle and name their properties, such as the number of corners.

- ☐ Give children an opportunity to make different 5-sided shapes on their pinboards. Encourage them to use mathematical vocabulary to describe the properties of a pentagon.
- ☐ Demonstrate cutting off the corners of a triangle to make a hexagon, and cutting the corners of a square (or rectangle) to make an octagon.
- ☐ Children sort a collection of 2-D shapes according to the number of sides or corners.

Things to say and ask

- ☐ *Imagine that I cut all 3 corners off this triangle. How many corners will the new shape have?* (6) *How many sides?* (6).
- ☐ *What if I cut all 4 corners off this square? How many corners will the new shape have?* (8)
- ☐ *How many different hexagons have we made on our pinboards?*
- ☐ *You could change the rules of the game. Keep rolling the dice and picking up straws. The first player to make 1 octagon, 2 hexagons and 3 pentagons is the winner.*

Answers

1 and **2** Child's own shapes.

Solid shapes

Activity Sheet 79

Objectives

Vocabulary

name, cone, cube, cuboid, cylinder, pyramid, sphere, flat, curved, straight, round, point, pointed, end, surface, side, face, edge, corner, circular

- ☐ Use the mathematical names for common 3-D shapes, including pyramid and cylinder
- ☐ Sort shapes and describe some of their features, such as edges, corners, faces.
- ☐ Make and describe shapes, pictures and patterns.
- ☐ Relate solid shapes to pictures of them.

Resources

set of solid shapes – cone, cube, cuboid, square-based cuboid, cylinder, sphere, triangle- and square-based pyramid (per group)

a red, blue and green pencil (per pair)

Teaching support

Misconceptions

Some children have difficulty in visualising 3-D shapes from pictures or drawings. Sketch dotted lines to help them see the shape of the hidden face.

The key ideas are that a cylinder has 2 circular faces, 2 curved edges and one curved face, while a pyramid has triangular faces that meet at a point, and the base can have 3 or more straight edges.

Children should be able to name and describe the cube, cuboid, cone and sphere.

- ☐ Give each child a 3-D shape. Pose questions that focus on its properties, e.g. shape of faces, number of faces, edges, corners.
- ☐ Display a set of 3-D shapes. Children should close their eyes while you describe one shape. Ask a child to pick up the described shape. Invite children to make up clues about a shape, and support them in using the appropriate mathematical vocabulary.

❏ *Hold up your shape if it has curved/straight edges … less/ more than 5 corners… 5 faces … rectangular faces only …*

❏ *Can you describe a shape for someone else to guess?*

Answers

1 b 2 cones **c** 3 cylinders **d** 3 pyramids

2 b 2 circles, 1 curved face **c** 1 square, 4 triangles **d** 4 triangles

3 left: red cylinder; middle: green pyramid; right: blue cone

Line symmetry

Activity Sheet 80

Objective

❏ Begin to recognise line symmetry.

Vocabulary

symmetrical, line of symmetry, fold, match, mirror line, reflection, pattern

Resources

poster paint (per group)

newsprint (per group)

mirror (per group)

2-D shapes (per group)

6 large squares: 2 red, 2 blue, 2 yellow (per group)

square, rectangle, right-angled triangle (per pair)

about 20 pegs (per pair)

pegboards (per pair)

elastic band (per pair)

ruler (per child)

mirror (per child)

colouring materials (per child)

blank paper or card (per child)

tracing paper (per child)

Teaching support

Misconceptions

Some left-handed children may need help in testing for line symmetry with a mirror.

The key idea is that the fold line is called the line of symmetry.

Introduce children to the new topic of line symmetry by:

▪ Investigating shapes made with paint blots. Remind children to begin spreading paint from the crease, and to fold over the painted side.

▪ Visualising, then testing with a mirror, classroom objects with a line of symmetry.

▪ Exploring the 2-D shapes that can be made by placing the mirror along one side of a 2-D shape.

▪ Place 3 large squares in a line, e.g. red, blue, yellow. Explore ways of adding the other set of 3 squares to make symmetrical patterns, e.g. in a line of 6 squares or in a 3 × 2 grid.

▪ Give pairs of children a pegboard, pegs and elastic band to act as the line of symmetry. In turn, children complete the other 'half' of the pegboard to make a symmetrical pattern.

Things to say and ask

❏ *The fold line or crease is the line of symmetry.*
❏ *Shapes that have 2 matching halves are symmetrical.*
❏ *Can you make a larger triangle? Do you always make a rectangle when you place your mirror along an edge of the square?*

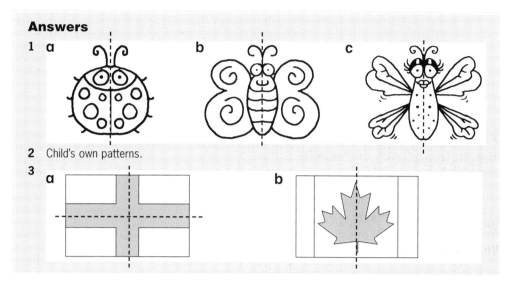

Answers

1 a   b   c

2 Child's own patterns.

3 a   b

Position

Activity Sheet 81

Objective

Vocabulary

left, right, higher, lower, next to, below, between, further away from, on the edge of, at the corner of

❏ Use mathematical vocabulary to describe position, direction and movement: for example, describe, place, tick, draw or visualise objects in given positions.

Resources
large 3 × 4 grid on card or on the board (per group)
6 different 2-D shapes (per group)
Blu-tack (per group)

Teaching support

Misconceptions
When the position of an object is relative to two other objects, check that the children use both position descriptors.

The key idea is for children to give the position of an object relative to another object.

Children should already be confident with the vocabulary of position: left, right, above, below, beside, between.

◻ Place a circle in the top left-hand corner of the grid. Introduce or elicit the phrase 'at the corner of'. Discuss that in placing a triangle next to the circle we have 2 possible positions and if we add the phrase 'lower than the circle' we pinpoint the position.

◻ Continue to place other 2-D shapes in the grid and give children opportunities to use the vocabulary listed above, for example, a child places a shape on the grid and the children offer suggestions of what your whispered instruction was.

◻ When all the shapes are placed in the grid, give the children further practice in identifying the shape from its positional description.

Things to say and ask

❏ *Where might the triangle go?*
❏ *Who can place the pentagon lower than the circle and on the edge of the grid?*
❏ *Which shape is above/below/next to/between...?*
❏ *What is higher/lower than...?*
❏ *Which shape is further away from the ... than the ...?*

Answers

1   **a**   next to;   **b**   higher than;   **c**   on the edge of;

2

Quarter turns and right angles

Activity Sheet 82

Objectives

Vocabulary

whole turn, half turn, quarter turn, left, right, clockwise, anticlockwise, right angle, straight line, route

- Recognise whole, half and quarter turns, to the left or right, clockwise or anticlockwise.
- Know that a right angle is a measure of a quarter turn, and recognise right angles in squares and rectangles.

Resources

large card showing a cross-axis (2 lines crossing at right angles) (per group)

4 large picture cards or toys, e.g. bus, train, car, plane (per group)

squares and rectangles in a range of sizes (per group)

paper circle (per child)

Teaching support

The key idea is that a right angle is a measure of a quarter turn.

Children should be able to recognise and make whole and half turns to the left and to the right.

- Place the cross-axis card on the floor with a picture card at the end of each axis.
- Ask a child to stand on the cross axis and face, say, the train. Discuss the amount of turn and direction of turn to face a different object. Introduce the terms quarter turn clockwise and anti-clockwise. Repeat for other children.
- Sketch a route from, say, the classroom to the school office. Elicit the route as '$\frac{1}{4}$ turn to the left, straight on, then $\frac{1}{4}$ turn to the right'. Ask two children who live near each other to describe the route to each other's house.
- Directly compare the corners of squares and rectangles. Children fold a paper circle to make a right angle tester. They use their 'tester' to find right angles in squares, rectangles and classroom objects.
- Using the cross-axis card place 4 right-angle testers round the origin to establish the link between the amount of turn and the number of right angles.

Things to say and ask

❏ *Kim made a quarter turn, clockwise and to the right. Make two quarter turns to the left. Which object do you face?*
❏ *How much turn is the same as two (or four) quarter turns?*
❏ *What can you tell me about the corners of a square and a rectangle?*
❏ *We use a small square to mark the right angle.*

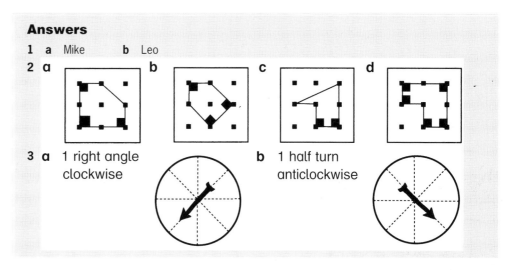

Answers
1 **a** Mike   **b** Leo
2 **a**   **b**   **c**   **d**
3 **a** 1 right angle   **b** 1 half turn
    clockwise   anticlockwise

Routes and mazes

Activity Sheet 83

Objective

Vocabulary

direction, journey, route, left, right, up, down, across, whole turn, half turn, quarter turn, right angle, straight line

❏ Give instructions for moving along a route in straight lines and round right-angled corners.

Resources
a 1p, 2p, 5p and 10p coin (per group)
large 3 × 2 grid of squares (per group)
counter (per pair)

Teaching support

Misconceptions
The most common misunderstanding is whether a turn is to the left or right.

The key idea is to demonstrate that if you turn to the left or right through a right angle, then you have made a quarter turn.

Children should be able to interpret the direction and movement instructions: up, down, across, along, turn

■ Place 4 coins on the large 3 × 2 grid. Explain that the object is to collect the most money by moving along, up or down but not diagonally and turning through a right angle to the left or right. Mark 2 squares 'start' and 'finish'. Invite a range of possible routes that could be used. Explain that a square cannot be visited more than once.

■ In question 1, ask children to describe the route they took.

Things to say and ask

❏ *In question 1, you can only visit each room once.*
❏ *What if you had different 'start' and 'finish' positions?*
❏ *In question 3, how many different safe routes can you find?*

Answers
1 29 mice caught in the following order: 6, 8, 1, 3, 7, 4.
2 turn left, along 1 square, turn right, up 2 squares, turn right, along 3 squares

Shape puzzles

Activity Sheet 84

Objectives

Vocabulary

square, rectangle, pentagon, hexagon, octagon, straight line, corner, side

❏ Solve mathematical problems or puzzles, recognise simple patterns and relationships, generalise and predict. Suggest extensions by asking 'What if …?' or 'What could I try next?'

❏ Explain how a problem was solved orally and, where appropriate, in writing.

Resources
pinboard (per child)
elastic band (per child)
ruler (per child)

Teaching support

Misconceptions
Remind children of the importance of lining up the dots, and of ruling straight lines. Inaccurate drawings will not reveal the square in question 2b.

The key idea is that drawing diagonal lines in a shape outline creates different shapes within the outline.

Children should be able to name the common 2-D shapes and describe some of their features, e.g. a pentagon has 5 sides and 5 corners.

▪ Use pinboards and elastic bands to check that children can construct pentagons.

▪ In question 1c, help children to see that the points 1, 3 and 4 form a straight line and the points 1, 4 and 5 form a large triangle. Repeat for points 2, 3 and 5.

▪ Ask children to explain how they found the additional triangles in question 3.

Things to say and ask

❏ *How many different shapes can you see inside the octagon?* (4 triangles, 1 square)
❏ *Can you find another shape?* (pentagon)
❏ *Tell me which numbers are at the corners of your pentagon.* (e.g. 8, 1, 2, 4 and 6)
❏ *How many more pentagons can you find?* (3)

Answers

1 a 3   b 3   c 5
2 a octagon   b square
3 Children can find a maximum of 12 triangles.

Pictures and patterns

Activity Sheet 85

Objectives

Vocabulary

triangle, triangular, square, pentagon, hexagon, octagon, straight line, corner, side

❏ Investigate a general statement about familiar shapes by finding examples that satisfy it.

❏ Explain how a problem was solved orally and, where appropriate, in writing.

Resources
plastic interlocking tiles (equilateral triangle, square, hexagon) or equivalent shapes with sides of matching length (per child)

Misconceptions

To help children see the continuous straight line made by joining the hexagon and equilateral triangle, ask them to use tiles of the same colour or to draw round the shape template and count the number of sides.

The key idea is to encourage problem-solving strategies. Children are encouraged to work systematically, look for a pattern and use the pattern to extend the problem.

Children should be able to name common 2-D shapes and describe some of their features, e.g. any shape that has 5 sides is a pentagon.

❑ Distribute squares and equilateral triangles. Investigate the number of sides of composite shapes made by joining 1, then 2, 3 and 4 equilateral triangles to the sides of the square. Ask children to predict the number of sides of the composite shape when 4 equilateral triangles are joined to the sides of the square.

❑ Distribute hexagons and equilateral triangles for Activity Sheet 85. Explain that a table is a useful way to record results. Elicit oral explanations of how the pattern works.

Things to say and ask

❑ *Who can guess the number of sides the shape will have when I join together one hexagon and one triangle? Why is it a pentagon?*
❑ *Who found a quick way to work out the number of fins for 5 octagon fish?*

> **Answers**
> **2** 2, 4, 6
> **3** The number of fins is going up in twos. You need double the number of fins for the number of fish.
> **4** 14, 20, 20, 25
> **5** 20 fins

Making a list

Activity Sheet 86

Vocabulary

list, count, score

❑ Solve a given problem by sorting, classifying and organising information in simple ways, such as in a list.

❑ Discuss and explain results.

> **Resources**
> 3 dice (per pair)
> paper and pencil (per child)

Misconceptions

Children may need to be reminded that a list has each item written below the previous one. They may also need a strategy for checking their totals in the game, such as writing each new number on a separate piece of paper next to their list, and checking it against each existing number from the top.

The key idea is that children use their skills and knowledge of list-making in the context of a game. They need to appreciate the advantages of recording in this way.

Children should have had experience of ordering numbers up to 30, and be able to add two or three single-digit numbers up to a total of 18. They will also need to be able to record these numbers.

❑ Discuss the purpose and organisation of a list.

❑ Establish that the purpose of writing information in a list is to make it easier to find out what you need to know.

❑ In the game, children will need to refer back to their own lists to find out whether they have any repeated numbers.

❑ It may be appropriate to support children's understanding of how the game is played. Children could also try playing the same game using 2 dice.

Things to say and ask

❑ *Why is it helpful to write your numbers in a list?*
❑ *What is the highest number you could get?*
❑ *Can you think of an even better way of recording your totals?*

Answers

1 a 3, 4, 5, 6, 7   **b** 22, 23, 24, 25, 26   **c** 16, 17, 18, 19, 20
    d 0, 1, 2, 3, 4   **e** 10, 11, 12, 13, 14   **f** 23, 24, 25, 26, 27

Using a table

Activity Sheet 87

Objectives

Vocabulary

table, between, discuss, split, most common, least common

❑ Solve a given problem by sorting, classifying and organising information in simple ways, such as in a simple table.

❑ Discuss and explain results.

Resources
1–50 number cards (per child)
red and blue pencils (per child)

Teaching support

Misconceptions
Children need to organise themselves in this activity. If necessary, show them how to place the cards in a pile, take one at a time and record it in the correct place on the table, and then discard it.

The key idea is that children organise numbers and comment on the outcomes, and respond to 'What if...?' questions. Deciding how to organise information is a central skill in data handling. At this stage, children are learning the range of possibilities available to them.

Children need to be familiar with reading and ordering numbers up to 50, and to have had experience of discussing their work.

■ Most support will be needed at the end of the activity, when children should discuss their work. Ask them to explain what they have done, and to comment on the outcomes. Encourage them to say which were the most and least common ranges of numbers to occur, and whether or not they think this would be the same if they repeated the activity. They can compare their results with other children.

Things to say and ask

❑ *Where would 21 go on your table?*
❑ *If you used all the cards in the 1–50 pack, what do you think the table would look like?*
❑ *Do you know any other numbers that would go in the last column?*
❑ *Which part of the table has the most numbers in? Are there any two sections that have the same number?*

Answers

1 b 20 8   **c** 40 1   **d** 30 2   **e** 30 7   **f** 30 0   **g** 50 3
    h 40 2   **i** 20 5

2 (Children will be identifying their own numbers for this activity.)

3 a

Numbers up to 10	Numbers from 11 to 20	Numbers from 21 to 30	Numbers from 31 to 40	Numbers from 41 to 50
	18	28, 30, 25	32, 37	41, 42, 46

    b 53

4 (Children will be identifying their own numbers for this activity.)

96

Tallying

Objectives

Vocabulary

tally, count, discuss

❑ Solve a given problem by sorting, classifying and organising information in simple ways.

❑ Discuss and explain results.

Resources
1-minute timer (per group of 3)

Teaching support

Misconceptions

The most common error is for children to make 5 tally marks before 'crossing the gate' ||||. Remind them that the cross counts as a mark, and help them to remember by counting *one, two, three, four, five* as you point at each mark.

The key idea is to give children experience of tallying. This is a useful way of keeping track of things as they happen. There is a formality attached to tallies; the five-bar gate symbol (||||) is used to represent 5. This makes counting the tallies easier, as they can be counted in 5s.

Children should have a sound knowledge of counting and recognising numbers up to 30. They should have had experience of oral counting in 5s.

▪ Ask children to count some things that move, e.g. people walking down the corridor, birds outside the window, cars driving past. When children need to keep track of more than 10 objects (when their fingers run out), explain that there is another way of keeping track.

▪ Show children how to represent 5 and larger numbers using tally marks.

▪ Practise using tallies by counting the moving objects again. Let children tell you each time a person/car/bird passes, and show them how to use tally marks to keep track.

▪ Remind children how to count in 5s, and show them how to count the tallies by counting in 5s.

▪ Explain that in this activity they will practise making tally marks and counting tallies.

Things to say and ask

❑ *Who blinked the most? Did you have to count all the marks to find out?*
❑ *How would you write 42 with tallies?*
❑ *Let me hear you count the tallies using fives.*

Answers

1	a	|||| I	b	|||| |||| II	c	|||| |||| |||| |||| I	d	|||| |||| IIII
	e	|||| |||| |||| I	f	|||| |||| ||||	g	|||| |||| |||| III	h	|||| |||| |||| IIII
2	a	8	b	13	c	14	d	2
	e	6	f	10	g	16	h	5

Making a pictogram

Objectives

Vocabulary

pictogram, label, title

❑ Solve a given problem by sorting, classifying and organising information in simple ways, such as in a pictogram.

❑ Discuss and explain results.

Resources
piece of blank paper (per pair)
scissors (per pair)
glue (per pair)

Misconceptions

The biggest challenge is collecting and representing the information in an organised way. Some children may benefit from using a data collection sheet as shown below.

Name	Number of brothers and sisters
Zelda	4
Zoe	3
Zac	0
Zarah	2

The key idea is that a pictogram is a pictorial version of a list, with pictures representing each item, rather than words or numbers. The two key skills are collecting the information in an organised fashion and transferring it on to the diagram, and 'reading' the pictogram once it is complete.

Children should have had experience of organising information in a table. Some children may be able to use tallying to collect the information they need for this activity. They will probably have seen pictorial representations before, but may not have used the word 'pictogram', or indeed gathered and represented their own information in this way.

- Explain that the purpose of the activity is to learn how to construct a pictogram. They will use it to answer the question: 'How many brothers and sisters do the children in our class have?'
- Children collect the information in pairs, by asking about 20 children in the class how many brothers and sisters they have. Discuss how they might collect this information, e.g. writing a list of names and numbers of brothers and sisters, or keeping a tally. Help them to decide which method they will use.
- Discuss the instructions on the Activity Sheet, and let children construct their pictograms.
- When they have finished, give them a chance to tell you one or two things that their charts show.

Things to say and ask

- *What does your pictogram tell us?*
- *Does your pictogram make it easier to find out if most of the children have brothers and sisters?*
- *Could we find out how many people have more than two brothers and sisters?*

Sorting money

Activity Sheet 90

Objectives

Vocabulary

pictogram, label, title, discuss

- Solve a given problem by sorting, classifying and organising information in simple ways, such as in a pictogram.
- Discuss and explain results.

> **Resources**
> mixed coins (real if possible): 1p, 2p, 5p, 10p, 20p, 50p, £1, at least 10 of each (per pair)

Teaching support

Misconceptions

Children may need prompting with comparing and interpreting their pictograms. Encourage them to look for things that are the same and things that are different about the two pictograms, and to look at the columns one at a time.

The key idea is that a pictogram is a pictorial version of a list, with pictures representing each item, rather than words or numbers. The two key skills are collecting the information in an organised fashion and transferring it on to the diagram, and 'reading' the pictogram once it is complete.

Children should have had experience of organising information in a table. They should also be familiar with the coins, although they do not have to be able to make amounts of money using them.

- Explain to children that they are going to compare handfuls of coins. In order to make it easier to compare, they are going to organise the coins by using them to make a pictogram.
- It makes the activity fun if they close their eyes to take their handfuls of coins. Then they can look at the handfuls, and guess who has more silver/bronze coins, or who has more £1 coins, before sorting them on to the pictogram.

❑ *Who has the most/fewest pennies?*
❑ *What is the total value of the 5p coins in your handful?*
❑ *Do you think that the pictogram of your next handful will look the same as this one?*

Guess my rule

Activity Sheet 91

Objectives

❑ Solve a given problem by sorting, classifying and organising information in simple ways.
❑ Investigate a general statement about familiar numbers by finding examples that satisfy it.
❑ Discuss and explain results.

Vocabulary

sort, classify, describe the rule

Resources
set of 0–20 number cards (per pair)
large set ring or Venn diagram drawn on a sheet of paper (per pair)
0–20 number line (optional) (per pair)

Teaching support

Misconceptions

Children may not use all the numbers in the set that belong to the chosen rule. Encourage them to check each card after they have placed it, and while their partner is trying to work out the rule.

Children could use a number line to help them check their numbers against the chosen rule, e.g. all the numbers between 10 and 15 should be grouped together on the number line. This strategy can also be used by the children who are trying to guess the rule. If they are having difficulty, they should ring the numbers from the set on the number line.

The key idea is to sort and classify numbers according to a given rule. The emphases are different for each player in the game: the child who is sorting the cards is finding examples to match a general statement, while the other child is trying to find out what that rule is by asking 'What if…?' questions, e.g. 'What if the rule is odd numbers? Do these numbers match?'

Children should have a sound knowledge of ordering numbers to 20 and beyond. They should also be aware of some of the properties of odd and even numbers.

◾ Demonstrate how to play the game by choosing some numbers according to a rule of your own, e.g. place all the single-digit numbers inside the set ring and the other numbers outside.

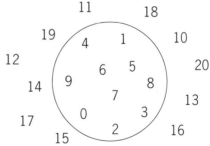

◾ Ask: *What is special about the numbers in the ring?* Establish that they are all single-digit numbers, and/or they are all less than 10. Explain that both answers are correct but that you were thinking of single-digit numbers.

◾ After children have played the game using the rules on the Activity Sheet they could invent their own rules.

❑ *How did you check your numbers?*
❑ *How did you know that this is not the rule? (Point to one of the inappropriate rules for the set.)*
❑ *Can you find two rules that give the same set of numbers?*

Answers
1   29, 1, 47, 13, 11, 25, 33, 43, 17

Making a block graph

Activity Sheet 92

Vocabulary

block graph, most/least popular, common, difference, represent, predict

❏ Solve a given problem by sorting, classifying and organising information in simple ways, such as in a block graph.

❏ Discuss and explain results.

Resources

Misconceptions

The most difficult part of this activity is keeping track of which shoes have been recorded. Encourage children to be systematic about recording, working around the class one table at a time.

If children have difficulty answering the questions, encourage them to look at one column at a time and find out how many pairs of shoes are represented in the column, then compare with the other columns.

The key idea is that a block graph is like a pictogram with no pictures. Unlike a pictogram, a block graph has a scale at the side, and a continuous block to represent each group, rather than individual pictures.

This activity brings together a number of skills. Children should have experience of collecting and sorting information in lists and tables, and have begun to use some of the language associated with sorting: more, fewer, most common, least common.

▪ Encourage children to predict the type of shoe that will be the most/least popular before they begin.

▪ If there is another type of shoe that is as popular as those listed, ask children to suggest how their graph might look. Let them use the 'others' column for this and re-label it.

▪ Explain that this type of graph is called a block graph, and elicit from children how it differs from a pictogram.

▪ When their graph is complete, discuss with children how the graph makes the information about shoes in the class easier to respond to, compared with the 'look around' that they had at the start. Explain that the purpose of a graph is to make information easier and clearer to understand.

▪ Discuss the questions on the sheet and if appropriate, ask children to write short answers.

❏ *How does the graph make it easier to find out which type of shoe is most popular?*
❏ *Do you think the graph for another class's shoes would look the same?*

Counting and writing numbers

Name ....

Let's practise

1 Write the missing numbers.

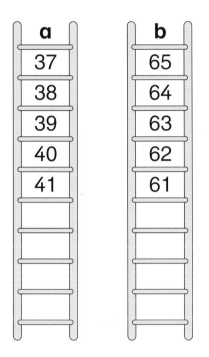 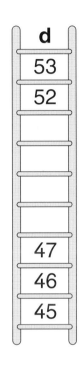 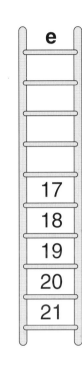 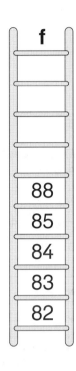

a	b	c	d	e	f
37	65	65	53		88
38	64	66	52		85
39	63				84
40	62			17	83
41	61			18	82
		71	47	19	
		72	46	20	
		73	45	21	

Let's play   A game for 2

You need: number cards from 0 to 100, 0–100 number line, 2 counters.

Take turns to:

Choose 2 number cards.

Tell your partner the numbers. Your partner puts a counter on both those numbers on the number line.

Say all the numbers between the counters.

Counting objects

Name ....

Let's practise

1 Write the totals.

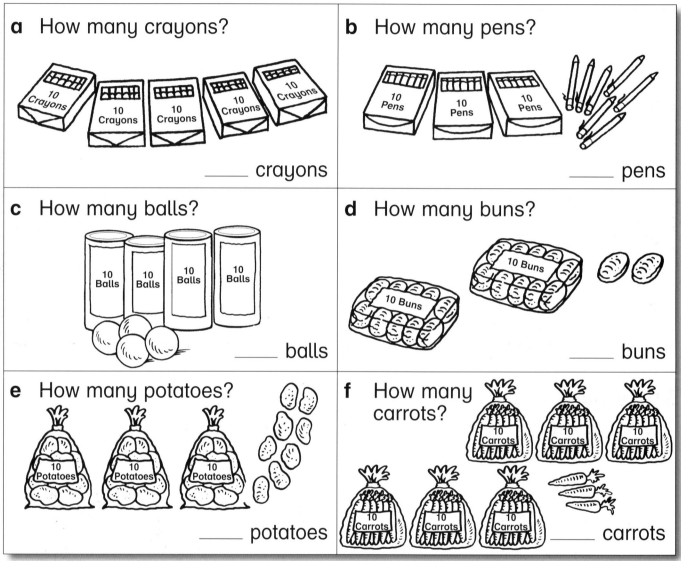

a How many crayons?

_____ crayons

b How many pens?

_____ pens

c How many balls?

_____ balls

d How many buns?

_____ buns

e How many potatoes?

_____ potatoes

f How many carrots?

_____ carrots

Let's investigate

2
- Choose something to count, like cubes or shells.
- Choose one of these numbers.
- Count out exactly that many objects.
- Group them in 10s and 1s.

Choose numbers of your own.
Collect groups of objects to match.

42
38
45
63
50

Counting in 10s

Name ....

Let's practise

1 Write the missing numbers.

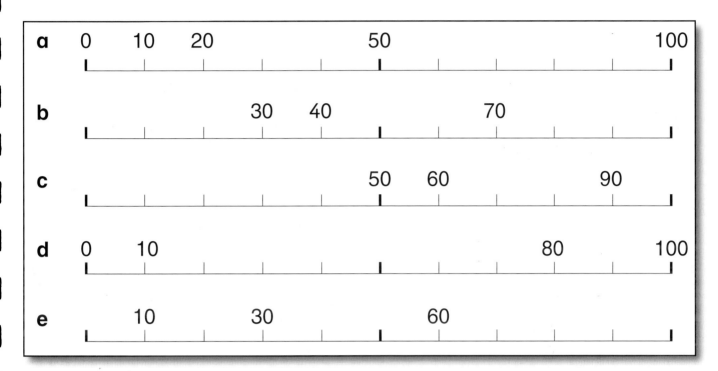

a   0   10   20   50   100

b   30   40   70

c   50   60   90

d   0   10   80   100

e   10   30   60

Let's play   A game for 2

You need: 3 sets of all the tens numbers from 10 to 100.

Take turns to pick
up a card.

Keep it if you need it.
Put it back, if you don't.

Try to collect 1 set of all
the 10s.

Counting on in 10s

Name ....

Let's practise

1 Jump on in 10s. Ring every number you land on.

a (34) 35 36 37 38 39 40 41 42 43 (44) 45 46 47 48 49 50 51 52 53 54 55 56 57 58 59 60 61 62 63 64 65 66 67

b (23) 24 25 26 27 28 29 30 31 32 33 34 35 36 37 38 39 40 41 42 43 44 45 46 47 48 49 50 51 52 53 54 55 56

c (16) 17 18 19 20 21 22 23 24 25 26 27 28 29 30 31 32 33 34 35 36 37 38 39 40 41 42 43 44 45 46 47 48 49

d (40) 41 42 43 44 45 46 47 48 49 50 51 52 53 54 55 56 57 58 59 60 61 62 63 64 65 66 67 68 69 70 71 72 73

e (4) 5 6 7 8 9 10 11 12 13 14 15 16 17 18 19 20 21 22 23 24 25 26 27 28 29 30 31 32 33 34 35 36 37

f (19) 20 21 22 23 24 25 26 27 28 29 30 31 32 33 34 35 36 37 38 39 40 41 42 43 44 45 46 47 48 49 50 51 52

g (61) 62 63 64 65 66 67 68 69 70 71 72 73 74 75 76 77 78 79 80 81 82 83 84 85 86 87 88 89 90 91 92 93 94

h (54) 55 56 57 58 59 60 61 62 63 64 65 66 67 68 69 70 71 72 73 74 75 76 77 78 79 80 81 82 83 84 85 86 87

Let's play   A game for 2

- Take turns.
- Choose one of the penguin numbers.
- Count back in 10s as far as you can.

Maths Spotlight 1. Copying permitted for purchasing school only. This material is not copyright free.

Counting on and back in 100s

Name ....

Let's practise

1 Continue the sequences.

a 1, 2, 3, 4, _____, _____, _____, _____, _____, _____

b 10, 20, 30, 40, _____, _____, _____, _____, _____

c 100, 200, 300, 400, _____, _____, _____, _____, _____

d 10, 9, 8, _____, _____, _____, _____, _____, _____, _____

e 100, 90, 80, _____, _____, _____, _____, _____, _____, _____

f 1000, 900, 800, _____, _____, _____, _____, _____, _____

2 You need: scissors and glue.
- Cut along all the dotted lines.
- Put the cards in order, from lowest to highest.
- Stick them in your book.

300	600	900	400
500	100	800	1000
	700	200	

Counting on and back in 2s

Name ....

Let's practise

1 Write the missing numbers.

a 2 4 6 8

b 1 3 5 9

c 5 7 9 15

d 20 18 16 8

Let's play   A game for 2

You need: number cards from 15 to 30, a 0–50 number line.

Take turns to:
- Take a card.
- Say the number.
- Count on in 2s to 50 (or 49).
- Your partner checks on the number line.

Play the game again.
This time count backwards.
Start at the number on the
card and count back in 2s to 0 or 1.

2 Choose one of these numbers:
11 4 13 16 15 19 8 6

Count on in 2s. Will you say '50' or '51'?
Guess first and then check.

Odd and even numbers

Name ....

Let's investigate

1 You need: 30 interlocking cubes.

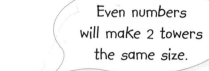

Even numbers will make 2 towers the same size.

a Take 10 cubes.
Use them to build 2 towers the same.

b Pick any number below.
Could you build 2 towers the same size using that number of cubes?
Work it out without using cubes.
Check using cubes.
Tick (✓) the numbers that work on this number track.

1	2	3	4	5	6	7	8	9	10	11	12	13	14	15	16	17	18	19	20	21	22	23	24	25	26	27	28	29	30
	✓														✓														✓

12   7   26   11

    18   17
              9

4   8

14   6   3

    13

c Tick all the other even numbers on the number track.

Counting in 3s

Name ....

Let's practise

1 Start at the cross. Colour every third number.
Say each number that you colour.

a

1	2	3 ✗	4	5	6	7	8	9	10	11	12	13	14	15	16

b

11	12 ✗	13	14	15	16	17	18	19	20	21	22	23	24	25	26

c

21 ✗	22	23	24	25	26	27	28	29	30	31	32	33	34	35	36

d

31	32	33 ✗	34	35	36	37	38	39	40	41	42	43	44	45	46

e

41	42 ✗	43	44	45	46	47	48	49	50	51	52	53	54	55	56

Let's investigate

2 Colour the multiples of 3 on these number squares.

a

1	2	3
4	5	6
7	8	9

b

1	2	3	4
5	6	7	8
9	10	11	12
13	14	15	16

c

1	2	3	4	5	6
7	8	9	10	11	12
13	14	15	16	17	18
19	20	21	22	23	24
25	26	27	28	29	30
31	32	33	34	35	36

d

1	2	3	4	5	6	7
8	9	10	11	12	13	14
15	16	17	18	19	20	21
22	23	24	25	26	27	28
29	30	31	32	33	34	35
36	37	38	39	40	41	42
43	44	45	46	47	48	49

3 Tell your teacher about the patterns you find.

Counting in 4s

Name ....

Let's practise

1 These patterns count in 4s.
There is a missing number in each
pattern. Write the missing number
in the correct place.

a	4	8	16	20	24	28	32
b	32	28	24	20	12	8	4
c	8	12	16	24	28	32	36
d	1	5	9	13	17	21	29

Let's play   A game for 2

You need: 1 calculator, 2 counters.

1	2	3	4	5	6	7	8	9	10
11	12	13	14	15	16	17	18	19	20
21	22	23	24	25	26	27	28	29	30
31	32	33	34	35	36	37	38	39	40
41	42	43	44	45	46	47	48	49	50

Take turns to:

■ Put a counter on 4 and count up in 4s.
 Move the counter each time.

■ Your partner enters 4 on the calculator and keeps adding 4 to check.

■ Leave the counter on the highest number you reach.

Counting in 5s and 10s

Name ....

Let's practise

1 **a** 5 + 15 = _____   **b** 15 + 5 = _____   **c** 15 – 5 = _____

   d 5 + 10 = _____   **e** 5 – 5 = _____   **f** 10 + 5 = _____

   g 10 – 5 = _____   **h** 20 + 5 = _____   **i** 20 – 5 = _____

   j 20 – 10 = _____   **k** 10 + 10 = _____   **l** 30 – 15 = _____

   m 15 – 10 = _____   **n** 20 + 10 = _____   **o** 30 – 10 = _____

Let's investigate

2 **a** Mark a tick (✓) on every fifth number.

   b Draw a smile (☺) on every tenth number.

0 ✓ ☺	1	2	3	4	5 ✓	6	7	8	9
10	11	12	13	14	15	16	17	18	19
20	21	22	23	24	25	26	27	28	29
30	31	32	33	34	35	36	37	38	39
40	41	42	43	44	45	46	47	48	49

3 Tick (✓) the sentences that are true.

   Cross (✗) the sentences that are false.

   a 35 is in the pattern of 5s.

   b All the numbers in the pattern of 5s are even.

   c All the numbers in the pattern of 5s end in 5.

   d All the numbers in the pattern of 10s end in 0.

   Now write 4 sentences of your own, 2 true and 2 false.

true	
true	
false	
false	

Counting in 2s

Name ....

Let's practise

1 Add 2 to each number.

a 4   b 10   c 20

d 2   e 6   f 8

g 22   h 12   i 10

j 18   k 24   l 30

Let's play   An activity for 2

You need: twenty 2p coins, a purse.

Take turns to:

- Put a 2p coin in the purse.
- Say the total amount of money that is in the purse. Now write it down.

- Keep going until you have used all the coins.

What do you notice about the last digit in your answers?

Continuing patterns

Name ....

Let's practise

1 Write the missing numbers.

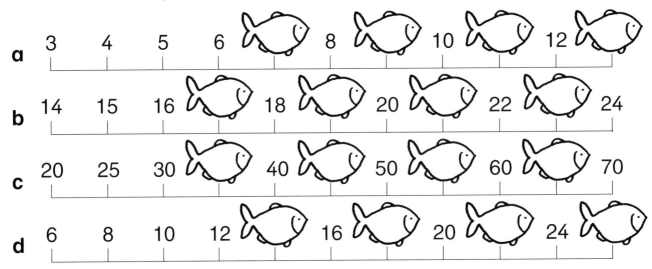

a 3   4   5   6   _   8   _   10   _   12   _

b 14   15   16   _   18   _   20   _   22   _   24

c 20   25   30   _   40   _   50   _   60   _   70

d 6   8   10   12   _   16   _   20   _   24   _

Let's play   A game for 2

You need: small counters.

Take turns to:

- Choose one of these numbers: 2   3   4   5   10.
- Start at 0. Count on in steps of your chosen number.
- Put a counter (of the same colour) on each number you say.
- Ask your partner to continue the pattern on the blank squares.

0	1	2	3	4	5	6	7	8	9
10	11	12	13	14	15	16	17	18	19
20	21	22	23	24	25	26	27	28	29
30	31	32	33	34	35	36	37	38	39

2 Which numbers belong in the pattern of 2s **and** 5s?

Number rules

Name ....

Let's practise

1 Write 3 of each kind of number.

a	Odd numbers				**b**	Numbers in the pattern of 3s			
c	Even numbers				**d**	Numbers in the pattern of 5s			
e	Numbers in the pattern of 10s				**f**	Numbers in the pattern of 2s			

Let's play   A game for 2

You need: number cards from 1 to 50.

Take turns to:
- Choose a whale.
- Find 5 numbers that fit the rule.
- Write the numbers.

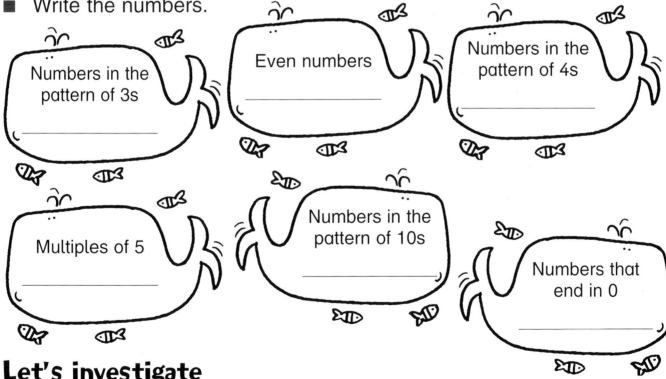

Odd numbers

Numbers in the pattern of 3s

Even numbers

Numbers in the pattern of 4s

Multiples of 5

Numbers in the pattern of 10s

Numbers that end in 0

Let's investigate

2 For each rule above think of 2 numbers greater than 50.
   Write them in the whale shapes too.

Explaining odd and even numbers

Name ....

Let's practise

1 Use odd numbers.

a ⬚ + ⬚ = 8

b ⬚ + ⬚ = 10

c ⬚ + ⬚ = 12

d ⬚ + ⬚ = 14

e ⬚ + ⬚ = 16

2 Use even numbers.

a ⬚ + ⬚ = 8

b ⬚ + ⬚ = 10

c ⬚ + ⬚ = 12

d ⬚ + ⬚ = 14

e ⬚ + ⬚ = 16

Let's solve problems

You need: counters.

3 These chimps have 21 marbles.
They each take an odd number of marbles.
Pip has 2 more than Bing.
Dong has 2 less than Bing.
There are no marbles left in the bag.
How many do they have each?

4 Repeat question 3 for 15 or 27 marbles.

Reading and writing numbers

Name ....

Let's practise

1 Write these numbers in figures.

   a seventeen _____   **b** twenty-three _____   **c** thirty-two _____

   d forty-eight _____   **e** seventy-one _____   **f** eighty-four _____

2 Choose two digit cards. Make a number. Write the number in figures, then words.

   a ☐☐   **b** ☐☐   **c** ☐☐

   _____   _____   _____

   d ☐☐   **e** ☐☐   **f** ☐☐

   _____   _____   _____

3 Write prices on the labels. Complete the sentences.

50p   This mouse costs _____.

This rabbit costs _____.

This guinea pig costs _____.

This hamster costs _____.

Understanding digits

Name ....

Let's practise

1 Draw lines to join the snakes to the correct number.

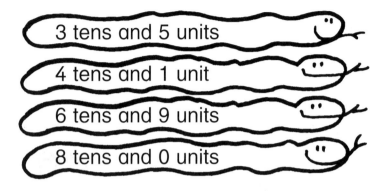

3 tens and 5 units   69

4 tens and 1 unit   80

6 tens and 9 units   35

8 tens and 0 units   41

2 Pick the two digits from the bag that make the number.

6   5   8   7

a nearest to 40   _56_   **b** nearest to 63 ____

c nearest to 60 ____   **d** nearest to 74 ____

3 Write four digits in the bag.
Pick the two digits that make the number.

a nearest to 30 ____   **b** nearest to 46 ____

c nearest to 75 ____   **d** nearest to 92 ____

Let's play   A game for 2

You each need: a set of 0 to 9 digit cards, 20 counters.

- Place your cards face down in a pile.
- Take turns to turn over the top 2 cards and make a 2-digit number.
- The player who has the larger number takes a counter.
- Replace your cards in the pack.

The winner is the first player to collect 10 counters.

Splitting numbers into tens and units

Name ....

Let's practise

1 Write the missing numbers.

   a 34 = __3__ tens and __4__ units   **b** 43 = ___ tens and ___ units

   c 81 = ___ tens and ___ unit   **d** 90 = ___ tens and ___ units

2 Draw lines to make different numbers.

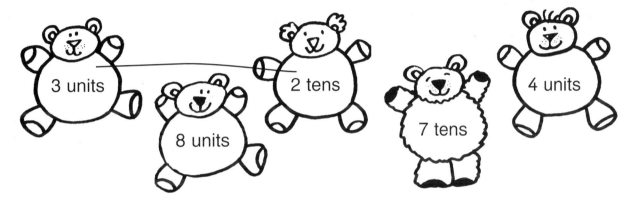

   a Write the numbers.

   _____   _____   _____   _____   _____

   b Now write the numbers in order. Start with the smallest.

   _____   _____   _____   _____   _____

Let's play   A game for 2

You need: place value cards.

Take turns to:

- Use a tens card and a units card to make a number.
- Your partner must say how many tens and how many units.
- Make as many numbers as you can.

This number has four tens and six units.

Comparing and ordering

Name ....

Let's practise

first ☆a ☆b ☆c ☆d ☆e ☆f ☆g ☆h ☆i ☆j ☆k ☆l ☆m

☆n ☆o ☆p ☆q ☆r ☆s ☆t ☆u ☆v ☆w ☆x ☆y ☆z **last**

1 Which letter is:

twenty-first _____   twenty-fourth _____   eighteenth _____?

2 In each pair, ring the number that is <u>less</u>.

a   56   65   **b**   37   41   **c**   61   16

d   83   38   **e**   40   51   **f**   89   91

Let's solve problems

3 Pick 5 cards from a set of 0 to 100 number cards.

Now put them in order. Write your numbers in order in the boxes.

smallest ▢ ▢ ▢ ▢ ▢ **largest**

Pick another 5 cards.

smallest ▢ ▢ ▢ ▢ ▢ **largest**

Let's play   A game for 2

You need: about 30 number cards from 0 to 100.

Take turns to:
- Take a card and place it face up.   21 37 58
- Take another card.
- If it is less than your first card, put it back in the pile.
  If it is greater, keep it.

The winner is the first to show 3 cards in order. Play several times.

Comparing numbers

Name ....

Let's practise

1 **a** Colour **red** the numbers that are more than 50.

   b Colour **yellow** the numbers that are less than 50.

23	67	33	91	15
42	72	17	63	55
14	49	30	52	47
9	51	28	80	32
39	69	16	98	40

2 Write these digits in the boxes to make two numbers.

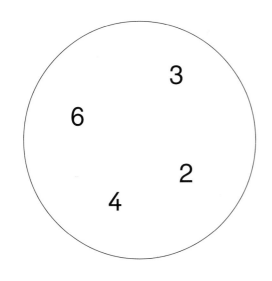

	smaller		larger	
a	3	2	6	4
b				
c				
d				

Can you find any more ways? _____

Let's solve problems

3 For each pair of numbers in question 2, write a number that lies between them.

45

_____ , _____ , _____ , _____ , _____ , _____ .

1 or 10 more or less

Name ....

Let's practise

1 Write the number that is 1 more.

a    b    c

37   45   79

2 Write the number that is 1 less.

a    b    c

55   71   80

3

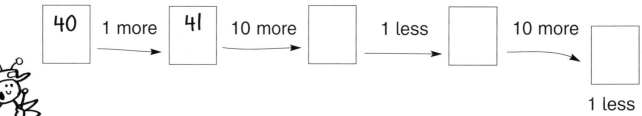

| 40 | 1 more | 41 | 10 more | | 1 less | | 10 more | |

1 less

1 more ← 1 more ← 10 less ← 10 less ←

10 more

1 more → 10 less → 1 less → 1 less →

4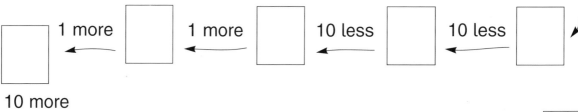

58 37 41 81 71 79 47 48 31 89

■ Colour a number on the centipede.
■ Find the number that is 10 more or 10 less.
■ Colour it in the same colour.
■ Use different colours for other pairs of numbers.

1 or 10 more or less puzzles

Name ....

Let's practise

1 Write the number that is 10 more.

a 27 / 37   b 51   c 69   d 90   e 43

2 Write the number that is 10 less.

a 44   b 59   c 81   d 79   e 90

3

| 1 more → | 1 less → | 10 more → | 10 less → |

Complete the labels.

a (15) | 10 more → | (25) | → | (24) | → | (34)

b (39) | → | (40) | → | (50) | → | (49)

c ( ) | 10 more → | (46) | 1 less → | ( ) | 10 more → | ( )

Let's play A game for 2

You need: number cards from 10 to 50.

- Put the cards in a pile. Take 6 cards each.
- Look for a pair of numbers that have a difference of 10.
- If you have a pair, put them on the table, face up.
- Take turns to turn over the top card.
- Take the card, if it makes a pair.

The winner is the first player to collect 4 pairs.

Ordering numbers

Name ....

Let's practise

1 Write these numbers in order. Start with the smallest.

a

| 53 | 35 | 87 | 26 |

b

| 71 | 69 | 78 | 94 |

_____   _____

2 The digit '6' is in each of these numbers.

| 16 | 26 | 56 |

Write all the numbers between 10 and 100 that have the digit 6.

| | | | | | | | | |

| | | | | | | | | |

Write all your numbers in order, starting with the smallest.

_____

_____

Let's investigate

3 7   3   2   9   1

How many different 2-digit numbers can you make with these cards?
Each card can only be used once in each number.

_____

Write your numbers in order, smallest to largest.

_____

Ordering and placing numbers

Name ....

Let's practise

1 Write the missing numbers.

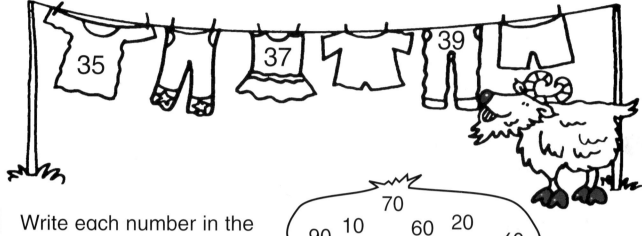

35   37   39

2 Write each number in the
bag on the number line.

70
90   10   60   20
   30   50   80   40

0										100

3 A 100-square has been cut into pieces.
Find the missing numbers.

a

37	38
	48

b

		41

c

	63

4 Write these numbers in the correct places
on the 100-square.

44	54	94	68
64	88	75	66
73	53	78	59
98	74	77	97
65	82	52	76
87	72	84	67

Colour the squares you
have written a number in.

								39	40
41	42								
									100

Estimating

Name ....

Let's solve problems

1 Estimate then count.

a

b

c
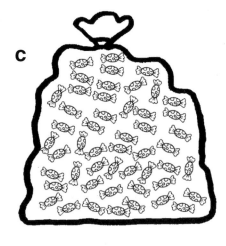

My estimate _____   My estimate _____   My estimate _____

My count _____   My count _____   My count _____

2 Estimate then count.

a How many chairs in the room?

estimate ____ count ____

b How many things on your desk?

estimate ____ count ____

c How many children in the classroom?

estimate ____ count ____

d How many words on this page?

estimate ____ count ____

Let's play   A game for 2

You need: counters.

■ Take a handful of counters. Put them on the table.
■ Estimate how many there are.
■ Ask your partner to estimate. Now count them.
■ The player who is nearer wins 1 point.

The winner is the first player to win 5 points.

Estimating and number lines

Name ....

Let's practise

1 Estimate then count the number of nuts.

a

b

My estimate _____

My count _____

My estimate _____

My count _____

2 Write the numbers the arrows point to.

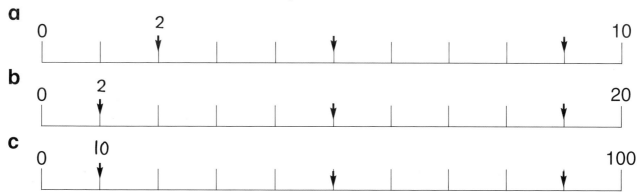

a

0   2   10

b

0   2   20

c

0   10   100

3 Write the halfway number on these number lines.

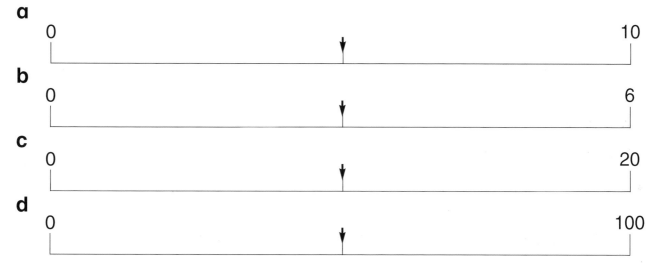

a

0   10

b

0   6

c

0   20

d

0   100

4 Now mark the number 5 on number lines b, c and d in question 3.

Rounding numbers

Name ....

Let's practise

1 Mark these numbers on the number line.

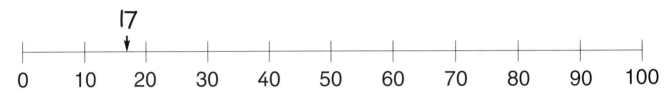

89   67   46   27   23   54   95

```
    17
     ↓
 ├────┼────┼────┼────┼────┼────┼────┼────┼────┼────┤
 0   10   20   30   40   50   60   70   80   90  100
```

2 Round each number to the nearest 10.

a 17 → ◯   **b** 23 → ◯   **c** 46 → ◯   **d** 54 → ◯

e 67 → ◯   **f** 89 → ◯   **g** 95 → ◯   **h** 72 → ◯

3 Write numbers that round to 30.

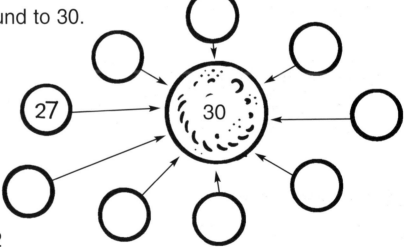

27 → 30

Let's play   A game for 2

You need: a set of 0 to 9 digit cards.

- ■ Spread the cards out face down.
- ■ Take turns to take 2 cards. Make a number with them, like this: | 3 | 7 |
- ■ Round the number to the nearest 10.
- ■ Colour this number in the grid. Replace the cards.

Can you colour all the numbers on your sheet before your partner?

10 20 30 40 50 60 70 80 90 100

Finding halves

Name ....

Let's practise

1 Put a ring around half of each set of animals.
Write the missing numbers.

a Half of 2 lions is ___ lion.

b  Half of 8 seals is ___ seals.

c  Half of 4 lizards is ___ lizards.

d  Half of ___ zebras is ___ zebras.

Let's investigate

2 You need: 20 counters.

> Remember to group your counters equally when you halve.

   a Find half of 10 counters. What is half of 10? _____

   b Find half of 12 counters. What is half of 12? _____

   c Find half of 14 counters. What is half of 14? _____

   d Look at the pattern in the answers.

   What is half of 16? _____

   What is half of 18? _____

   What is half of 20? _____

Finding quarters

Name ....

Let's practise

1 Put a ring around one quarter of each set of animals.
Write the missing numbers.

a One quarter of 4 koalas
is ___ koala.

b One quarter of 8 parrots
is ___ parrots.

Let's investigate

2 Get 40 cubes.

a Find one quarter of 12 cubes.

What is one quarter of 12? _____

b Find one quarter of 16 cubes.

What is quarter of 16? _____

c Find one quarter of 20 cubes.

What is quarter of 20? _____

d Find one quarter of 24 cubes.

What is quarter of 24? _____

e Look at the pattern in the answers.

What is quarter of 28? _____

What is quarter of 32? _____

What is quarter of 36? _____

What is quarter of 40? _____

Remember to group your cubes equally when you quarter them.

Half puzzles

Name ....

Let's practise

1 Tick (✓) the shapes that are divided into 2 equal parts.

Remember that the 2 parts are only halves if they are the same size.

a

b

c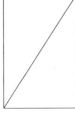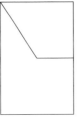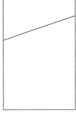

d

2 Colour half of each shape.

a **b** **c** 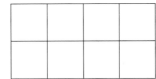 **d**

Let's investigate

3 **a** Draw a line in each shape to make 2 unequal parts.

 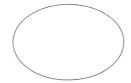  

b Draw a line in each shape to make 2 equal parts.

 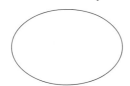  

Quarter puzzles

Name ....

Let's practise

1 Tick the shapes that
are divided into 4 equal parts.

Remember that the 4
parts are only quarters if
they are the same size.

a

b

c
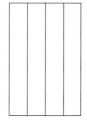 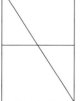  

d

2 Colour one quarter of each shape.

a
b
c
d

Let's investigate

3 **a** Draw lines in each shape to make 4 **unequal** parts.

 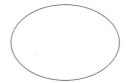 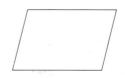

b Draw lines in each shape to make 4 **equal** parts.

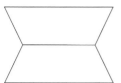 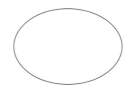 

Halves and quarters

Name..

Let's practise

1 Use these words. (one) (two) (four) (quarter) (half)

a The square has two equal parts.

Each part is called one _____.

b The circle has four equal parts.

Each part is called one _____.

c The rectangle has _____ equal parts.

Each part is called _____ half.

d The triangle has _____ equal parts.

Each part is called one _____.

Let's investigate

2 **a** Draw a line in each square to show two halves.
Show different ways.

b Draw lines in each square to show four quarters.
Show different ways.

Name ....

Let's practise

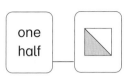

1 Darw lines to match the cards in as many ways as you can.

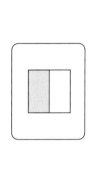

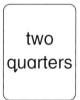
two quarters

one quarter

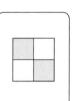

one half

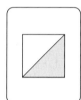

Let's play   A game for 2

You need: a fraction dice, a coloured pencil (each).

- Take turns to roll the dice.
- Put a tick (✓) in your table to record what the dice says.
- Colour that fraction on one of the large squares.
- The winner is the first player to colour all 4 large squares correctly.

Player 1 name _____	
one half	
one quarter	

Player 2 name _____	
one half	
one quarter	

Practising with fractions

Name ....

Let's practise

1 Write the missing words. (whole) (quarter) (half)

a ▦ and ▦ make one _____.

b ▦ and ▦ make one _____.

c ▦ and ▦ make three _____.

d ▦ and ▦ make one _____.

Let's play   A game for 2

You need: a set of fraction cards each.

Take turns to turn over your top card.

SAME!

If they are the same, say Same! The first one to say **same** gets the cards.

Two quarters is the same size as one half.

Try to get all the cards.

More practice with fractions

Name ....

Let's practise

1   Write the missing words.   (one)   (two)   (half)   (quarter)

one whole square

a   This is _____ _____ of the whole square.

b   This is _____ _____ of the whole square.

c   This is _____ _____ of the whole square.

d   This is _____ _____ of the whole square.

Let's play   A game for 2

You need: a fraction dice, a set of coloured fraction pieces (each).

- Take turns to throw the dice. Pick up a matching fraction piece.
- If it will fit, put it in your square. If not, put it back.
- The winner is the first player to fill their square exactly with fractions.

Player 1

Player 2

Understanding addition

Name ....

Let's practise

1

a 4 + 5 =

b 7 + 4 =

c 6 + 7 =

d 7 + 8 =

e 9 + 6 =

f 7 + 7 =

Let's play   A game for 2

You need: two 0–9 dice, a red and a blue pencil, 1 sheet between you.

Take turns to:

- Roll the two dice and add the numbers together.
- Colour the square red (player 1) or blue (player 2).
- Fill the grid.

5	1	7	14	6	2
15	4	11	8	11	18
6	10	17	12	3	18
8	6	2	0	8	6
13	15	9	16	12	8
12	10	9	6	7	10

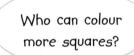

Who can colour more squares?

Let's investigate

2   Write six addition sums with the answer 12.

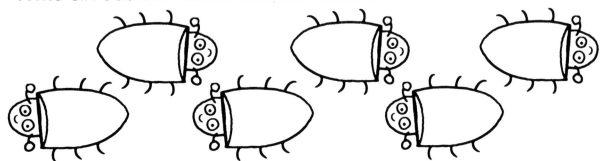

Missing numbers

Name ....

Let's practise

1 Write the missing numbers.

a 17 + 5 = 22

b 4 + 25 =

c 16 + 7 =

d 8 + 19 =

e 7 + 15 =

f 6 + = 20

g 7 + = 27

h 24 + = 30

i + 30 = 50

Let's solve problems

2 Write the missing numbers.

a 16 birds are on the grass. 4 more come. How many now? _____

b 12 frogs are in the pond. 6 more jump in. How many now? _____

c _____ cats sat on the mat. 9 more sit. There are 17 now.

d 23 cows are in a field. _____ more come. There are 30 now.

e _____ children are in the pool. 21 more jump in. There are 32 now.

f 34 bats are in the air. _____ more fly. There are 43 now.

Adding more than two numbers

Name ....

Let's practise

1   **a**   6 + 5 + 4 =    **b**   2 + 3 + 8 =

    c   6 + 5 + 10 =   **d**   8 + 12 + 2 =

    e   3 + 11 + 7 =   **f**   7 + 6 + 4 =

2   Colour 3 shells that make 24.

a

| 5 | 12 | 15 | 7 |

b

| 6 | 9 | 4 | 14 |

3   Colour 3 starfish that add to 100.

a

10   30   60   20   40

b

50   20   30   70   80

Let's investigate

4   Write three numbers that have a total of 20. ___ ___ ___

Can you think of three different numbers? ___ ___ ___

Let's play   A game for 2

You need: 3 dice, a different-coloured pencil for each player.

- Take turns to roll the dice and add the 3 numbers together.
- Colour that number on the grid.
- The winner is the first player to colour 3 numbers in a line.

3	7	15	9	8
12	11	17	6	11
5	10	8	10	18
14	9	13	16	4

Near doubles

Name ....

Let's practise

1 **a** 12 + 12 = ◯ **b** 13 + 13 = ◯ **c** 14 + 14 = ◯

Let's investigate

2 Colour a number in the grid.
- Double your number and add one.
- Double your number and take away one.
- Write both answers in the pairs of duck feet.

20	12	6	10
7	15	14	4
11	8	13	9

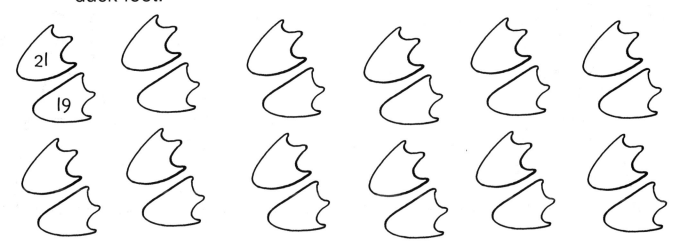

What do you notice? _____

3 Draw hats on 2 ducklings whose numbers add to the number in the egg.

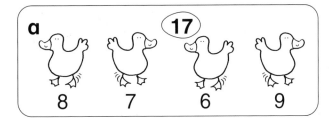

a 17
8   7   6   9

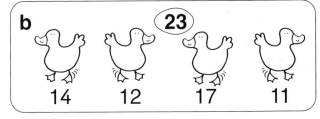

b 23
14   12   17   11

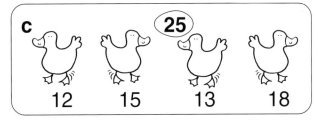

c 25
12   15   13   18

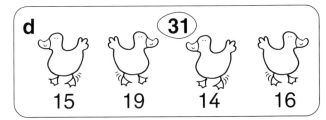

d 31
15   19   14   16

Adding in your head

Name ....

Let's practise

1 Count on from the larger number.

a 23 + 5 =

b 5 + 23 =

c 32 + 7 =

d 6 + 34 =

e 8 + 25 =

f 9 + 33 =

g 60 + 30 =

h 30 + 50 =

i 20 + 70 =

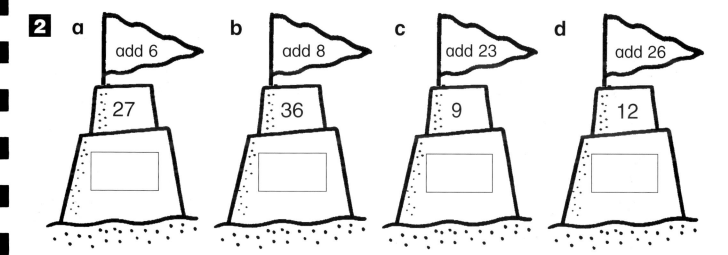

2 **a** add 6 — 27

b add 8 — 36

c add 23 — 9

d add 26 — 12

Let's play   A game for 2

You need: a 1–10 dice,
number cards from 10 to 40.

- Take turns to roll the dice and pick a card.
- Add the numbers.
- Write this as 2 addition sentences.

6 + 32 = 38
or
32 + 6 = 38

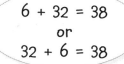

_____   _____

_____   _____

_____   _____

Splitting numbers

Name ....

Let's practise

1 Use the coins to help with these sums.

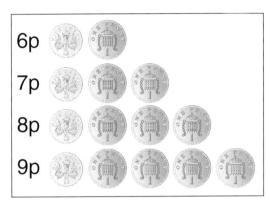

a 6p + 7p = (13p)   **b** 7p + 8p = (   )

c 9p + 6p = (   )   **d** 8p + 6p = (   )

e 15p + 9p = (   )   **f** 15p + 7p = (   )

g 25p + 8p = (   )   **h** 25p + 6p = (   )

Let's solve problems

2 Sam has 14p. He buys 2 sweets. Which sweets could he buy?

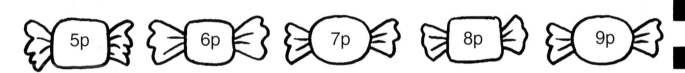

_____ + _____   _____ + _____   _____ + _____

_____ + _____   _____ + _____   _____ + _____

3 Use the coins to make the totals.

11p = (coins)   [   ] + [   ] = 25p

12p = (coins)   [   ] + [   ] = 24p

13p = (coins)   [   ] + [   ] = 26p

14p = (coins)   [   ] + [   ] = 27p

Pairing numbers

Name ....

Let's practise

1 Make each sum total 20.

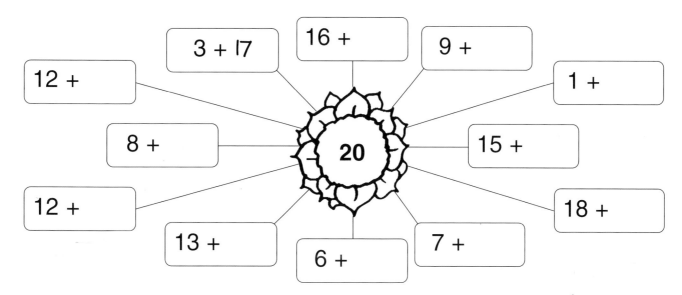

3 + 17	16 +
12 +	9 +
8 +	1 +
12 +	15 +
13 +	18 +
6 +	7 +

20

2 Use different colours to show pairs of numbers that add to 100.

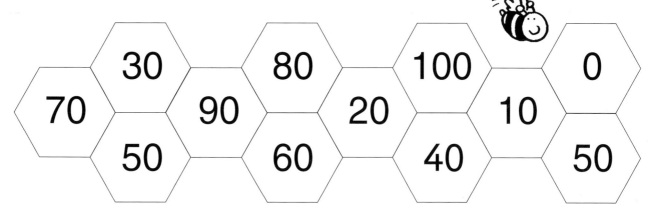

30 80 100 0

70 90 20 10

50 60 40 50

Let's play   A game for 2

You will need: a 1–20 dice and 20 counters.

- Take turns to roll the dice.
- What must be added to make 20?
- The first player to say the correct answer wins a counter.
- Who has more counters after 20 goes?

Adding and subtracting

Name ....

Let's practise

1

| 14 | 15 | 16 | 17 | 18 | 19 | 20 | 21 | 22 | 23 | 24 | 25 | 26 | 27 |

a 15 + 6 = _____   21 – 6 = _____

b 14 + 11 = _____   25 – 11 = _____

c 18 + 8 = _____   26 – 8 = _____

2 Write the missing numbers.

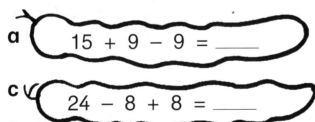

a 15 + 9 – 9 = _____

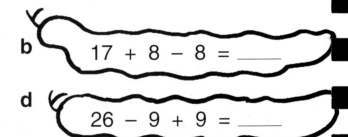

b 17 + 8 – 8 = _____

c 24 – 8 + 8 = _____

d 26 – 9 + 9 = _____

Let's solve problems

3 You need: 2 sets of 0 to 9 digit cards.

- Place the cards face down in a pile.
- Take turns to turn over the top 2 cards.
- Write an addition sentence using these 2 numbers.
- Now write a subtraction sentence using these **3** numbers.

5   **8**

Understanding subtraction

Name ....

Let's practise

1 a 6 − 3 = 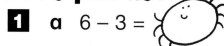   b 7 − 4 =   c 8 − 5 =

d 9 − 3 =   e 8 − 2 =   f 10 − 4 =

Let's play   A game for 2

You need: two 0–9 dice, a red and a blue pencil,
1 sheet between you.

Take turns to:

- Roll the 2 dice and find the difference between the numbers.
- Is the answer on a white ball?
- If it is, colour the ball red (player 1) or blue (player 2).

6	2	7	9	5	3
0	4	2	3	4	8
5	4	7	9	3	5
7	6	2	0	8	1
2	5	9	1	6	8
0	1	2	6	7	3

Who can colour more balls?

Let's investigate

2   Write subtraction sentences with the answer 7.

10 − 3 = 7

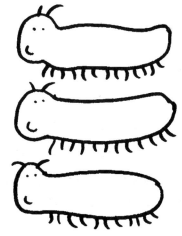

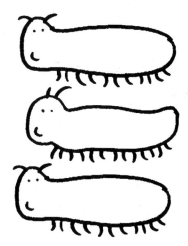

Find the missing numbers

Name ....

Let's practise

1 a 15 − 4 = 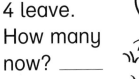 b 18 − 5 =  c 14 − 8 =

d 14 − ⬭ = 5 e 18 − ⬭ = 15 f 25 − ⬭ = 19

Let's solve problems

2

a 17 rabbits are on the grass. 4 leave. How many now? ____	**b** 25 bats are in a cave. ____ leave. There are 13 now.
c 26 ducks are in the pond. 15 fly away. How many now? ____	**d** 30 balloons are in the air. ____ go pop! There are 18 now.
e 32 sharks are in the sea. ____ swim away. There are 15 now.	**f** 32 lions are on the plain. ____ walk away. There are 21 now.

3 Look at the number sentences in question 1.
Choose 3 of these and make up your own word problems.

What's the difference?

Name ....

Let's practise

1 Count up from the smaller number.

14	15	16	17	18	19	20	21	22	23	24	25	26	27

a $19 - 14 =$

b $21 - 16 =$

c $22 - 15 =$

d $25 - 18 =$

e $26 - 15 =$

f $27 - 14 =$

Let's solve problems

2 **a**

I have 43p

I have 38p

difference is _____ p

b

I have 51p

I have 45p

difference is _____ p

Let's play   A game for 2

You need: a 1–20 dice, counters.

Take turns to:
- Roll the dice twice. Write the numbers.
- Work out the difference between them.
  Check on the number track.
- Take that number of counters.
- Have 5 turns each.
- The winner is the player with more counters.

0	1	2	3	4	5	6	7	8	9	10	11	12	13	14	15	16	17	18	19	20

Adding and subtracting 9 and 11

Name ....

Let's practise

1 **a** 16 + 9 =

b 17 − 9 =

c 18 + 11 =

d 19 + 9 =

e 28 − 11 =

f 32 + 11 =

g 26 − 9 =

h 31 − 11 =

i 30 − 11 =

2 Complete the trail.

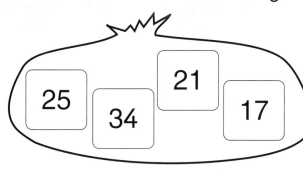

27 + 9

36 + 11

____ + 9

____ − 11

____ − 9

____ end

Let's investigate

3 Choose a card from each bag.

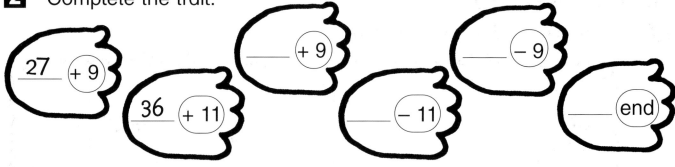

25   21   34   17

+ 11   − 11   + 9   − 9

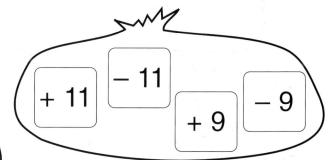

How many sums can you make?

25 + 9 = 34

Adding and subtracting 19 and 21

Name ....

Let's practise

1 **a** 20 + 19 =  **b** 28 − 19 = **c** 25 + 21 =

d 32 − 21 = **e** 27 + 19 = **f** 36 − 19 =

g 26 + 21 = **h** 40 − 21 = **i** 34 + 19 =

Let's investigate

2 Choose a card from each board.

38   27   41   56

+ 19   − 19   + 21   − 21

How many sums can you make?

27 + 19 = 46

3 29 —+19→ —+21→ —−19→ —+21→ —−19→

Subtractions and additions

Let's practise

1 a b

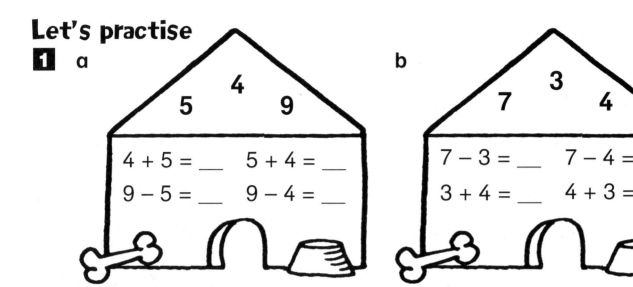

4 + 5 = __ 5 + 4 = __

9 − 5 = __ 9 − 4 = __

7 − 3 = __ 7 − 4 = __

3 + 4 = __ 4 + 3 = __

Let's investigate

2 Use the numbers in the roof to write 4 number facts.

a b

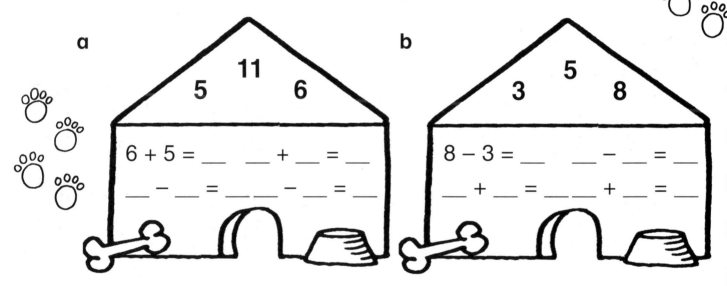

6 + 5 = __ __ + __ = __

__ − __ = __ __ − __ = __

8 − 3 = __ __ − __ = __

__ + __ = __ __ + __ = __

3 Use larger numbers to write a set of 4 number facts.

Adding and subtracting in your head

Name ....

Let's practise

1 Write the missing answers.

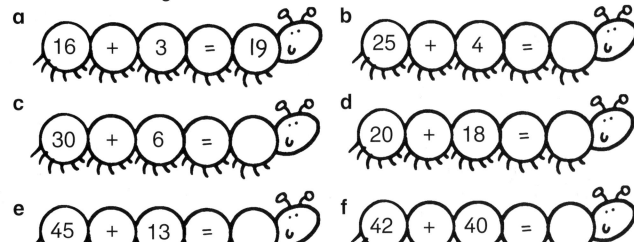

a   16 + 3 = 19

b   25 + 4 =

c   30 + 6 =

d   20 + 18 =

e   45 + 13 =

f   42 + 40 =

Let's investigate

2 Write your own sums in the caterpillars.

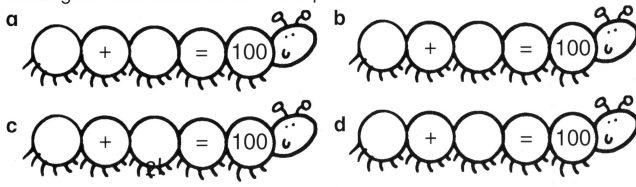

a   ◯ + ◯ = 100

b   ◯ + ◯ = 100

c   ◯ + ◯ = 100

d   ◯ + ◯ = 100

3 Find the difference. Write the answer in the body.

a   27 – 6 = _____   b   36 – 4 = _____   c   68 – 6 = _____

d   59 – 4 = _____   e   37 – 12 = _____   f   70 – 30 = _____

g   28 – 14 = _____   h   50 – 20 = _____   i   55 – 20 = _____

Number towers

Name ....

Let's practise

1 Add each pair of numbers.

a
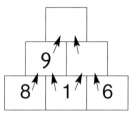

b
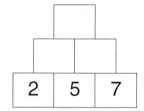

c
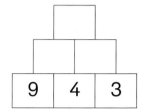

d
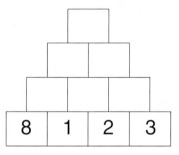

e
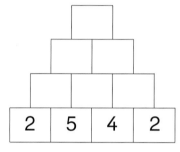

f
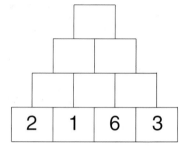

2 Find the difference between each pair of numbers.

a
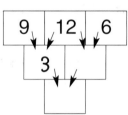

b
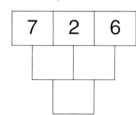

c
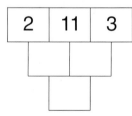

d
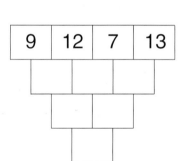

e
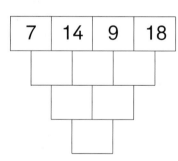

f
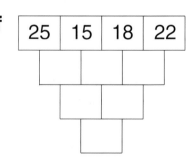

Let's investigate

3 Make some number towers of your own in your book.

Solving simple problems

Name ....

Let's practise

1 Write the scores for these games.

a 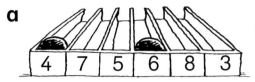 score
10

b 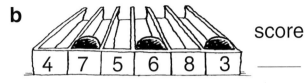 score
_____

c  score
_____

d  score
_____

e score
_____

f score
_____

Let's solve problems

2 Fill in the missing amounts. Tick who has more money in each pair.

a I had £24 but I spent £6.

I now have _____

b I had £8 and was given £12 more.

I now have _____

c I had £12. I spent half of this.

I now have _____

d I had no money but was given £3 and then £4.

I now have _____

e I had £15. I spent £7 but was given £3 more.

I now have _____

f My sister had £7. I had twice as much as her but spent £2.

I now have _____

Recognising coins

Name ....

Let's solve problems

1 Place coins in the correct places.

2 Follow a trail from start to finish.
Write the amounts and find the total.
Do this for other trails.

> 2p + 50p + £2 + 20p = £2·72

3 Which is the largest possible total? _____

4 Which is the smallest possible total? _____

Finding totals and using coins

Name ....

Let's practise

1 How much is in each purse?

a    b 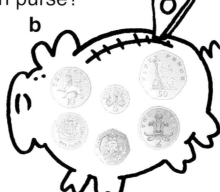   c

_____   _____   _____

Let's solve problems

2 In your book draw the coins needed to buy each toy.

a    b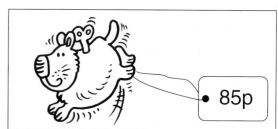

c 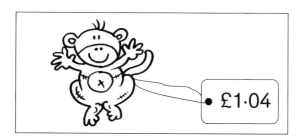   d

3 I bought a dinosaur. It cost more than £1.
I paid the exact price using 3 coins.
What could the dinosaur have cost?

£1 + 10p + 2p = £1·12

Giving change

Name ....

Let's solve problems

1 How much change from 50p?

a  •30p

That's _20p_ change, please.

b  •39p

That's _____ change, please.

c  •25p

That's _____ change, please.

d  •41p

That's _____ change, please.

e  •28p

That's _____ change, please.

f •36p

That's _____ change, please.

2 I bought a fish and paid with a £1 coin.
I was given **3** coins as change.
What could the fish have cost?

change   cost   84p

Begin to multiply

Name ....

Let's practise

1 **a**   4 lots of 2 cats

_____ × 2 = _____

b   3 lots of 2 frogs

_____ × 2 = _____

c   5 groups of 2 fish

_____ × 2 = _____

d   7 groups of 2 birds

_____ × 2 = _____

2 **a**   _____ lots of 10 worms

_____ × _____ = _____

b   _____ lots of 10 beetles

_____ × _____ = _____

c   _____ groups of 10 snails

_____ × _____ = _____

3   Draw the balls and hats and write the missing numbers.

a

3 lots of 10 balls

$3 \times 10 =$ _____

b

8 groups of 2 hats

$8 \times 2 =$ _____

More multiplying

Name ....

Let's investigate

1 **a** Use a red pencil.
Draw rings to show 5 lots of 3.

b Use a blue pencil.
Draw rings to show 3 lots of 5.

c Use × and = to write 2 number sentences to describe this array.

_____

2 **a** Use red to show 4 groups of 5.

b Use blue to show 5 groups of 4.

c Write 2 number sentences.

Let's play   A game for 2

You need: about 24 counters.

Take turns to:

■ Take a small handful of counters.
■ Count them and give them to your partner.
■ Your partner tries to arrange them as an array. (Not 1 line.)
■ Record the arrays you make, scoring 1 point for each.
■ The first player to reach 10 points is the winner.

Multiplication puzzles

Name ....

Let's practise

1

a $5 \times \boxed{} = 50$ **b** $7 \times 2 = \boxed{}$ **c** $\boxed{} \times 2 = 12$

d $8 \times \boxed{} = 16$ **e** $8 \times 10 = \boxed{}$ **f** $\boxed{} \times 10 = 90$

2 **a** $4 \times 5 = \boxed{}$ **b** $3 \times \boxed{} = 15$ **c** $\boxed{} \times 10 = 40$

d $6 \times 5 = \boxed{}$ **e** $2 \times \boxed{} = 18$ **f** $\boxed{} \times \boxed{} = 16$

Let's solve problems

3 **a** 3 children have 10 toys each.
How many toys?

$3 \times 10 =$

b 5 horses in a field.
How many legs?

c Jake has 6 eggs. Jo has twice as many.
How many eggs does Jo have?

d 7 rabbits in a burrow.
How many ears?

e 8 children have 10 stickers each.
How many stickers?

f Write your own word problem.

Doubles and halves

Name ....

Let's practise

1　**a**　Double 3 = _____　　**b**　Double 4 = _____　　**c**　Double 5 = _____

2　Count the fish.
Double the number. Draw a line to the new number.

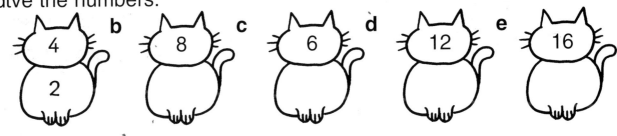

a　　　　**b**　　　　**c**　　　　**d**

| 1 | 2 | 3 | 4 | 5 | 6 | 7 | 8 | 9 | 10 | 11 | 12 | 13 | 14 | 15 | 16 | 17 | 18 |

3　Halve the numbers.

a 4 / 2　　**b** 8　　**c** 6　　**d** 12　　**e** 16

4　Write the missing numbers.

a　[10] Halve this number. → [ ] Double your answer. → [ ]

b　[14] Halve this number. → [ ] Double your answer. → [ ]

What do you notice? _____

Let's play　A game for 2

You need: a 0–9 dice, 20 counters.

- Take turns to roll the dice.
- What is double this number?
- The first player to say the correct answer wins a counter.
- The winner is the first player to collect 10 counters.

Division as sharing

Name ....

Let's practise

1 Share equally.

a
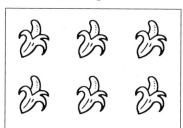

 3   3

$6 \div 2 =$ ___3___

b
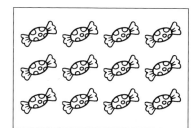

☐   ☐

$12 \div 2 =$ _____

c
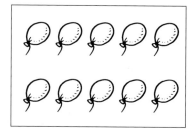

☐   ☐

$10 \div 2 =$ _____

d
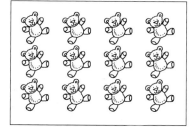

☐   ☐   ☐

$12 \div 3 =$ _____

e
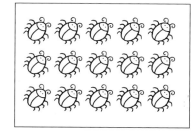

☐   ☐   ☐

$15 \div 3 =$ _____

f
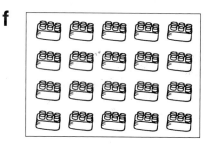

☐   ☐   ☐   ☐

$20 \div 4 =$ _____

Let's solve problems

2 Share 12 cubes equally.

   a 12 cubes between 2. How many each? _____

   b 12 cubes between 4. How many each? _____

   c 12 cubes between 6. How many each? _____

3 Share equally.

   a $6 \div 3 =$ (2)   **b** $12 \div 3 =$ ( )   **c** $18 \div 3 =$ ( )

   d $16 \div 4 =$ ( )   **e** $24 \div 4 =$ ( )   **f** $30 \div 5 =$ ( )

Division as grouping

Name ....

Let's solve problems

1 You need: 12 cubes.

   a How many groups of 2? _____   **b** How many groups of 3? _____

   c How many groups of 4? _____   **d** How many groups of 6? _____

2 You need: 20 cubes.

   a How many groups of 2? _____   **b** How many groups of 4? _____

   c How many groups of 5? _____   **d** How many groups of 10? _____

3

10 cubes		
group into 2s	__5__ groups	$10 \div 2 =$ __5__
group into 5s	_____ groups	$10 \div 5 =$ _____
group into 10s	_____ group	$10 \div 10 =$ _____

4

18 cubes		
group into 2s	_____ groups	$18 \div 2 =$ _____
group into 3s	_____ groups	$18 \div 3 =$ _____
group into 6s	_____ groups	$18 \div 6 =$ _____

Division problems

Name ....

Let's practise

1

a $60 \div 10 = \boxed{}$

b $16 \div \boxed{} = 8$

c $\boxed{} \div 10 = 7$

d $12 \div 2 = \boxed{}$

e $40 \div \boxed{} = 4$

f $\boxed{} \div 2 = 10$

Let's solve problems

2 $\boxed{} \div \boxed{} = 6$ How many different ways can you find to solve this puzzle? _____

3 **a** Two children share 18 sweets equally. How many each? _____

b Thirty children are split into 5 equal groups. How many in each group? _____

c I have 12 wheels. How many model cars can I make? _____

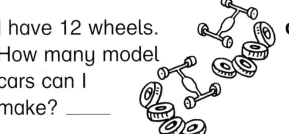

d Twenty apples are shared equally between 10 children. How many each? _____

Let's play   A game for 2

You need: a set of cards of even numbers 2 to 20, a '÷ 2' card, colouring pencils.

Place the '÷ 2' card on the table.

- Take turns to turn over a number card.
- Put it in front of the '÷ 2' card.
- Find the answer and colour the brick.
- Put your card back in the pile.

Who colours all their bricks first?

	6	2	
3	1	8	
	5	7	
4	9	10	

Halves and doubles

Name ....

Let's solve problems

1 Pick a number on a card.
Double it.
If the answer is in the grid,
colour it.

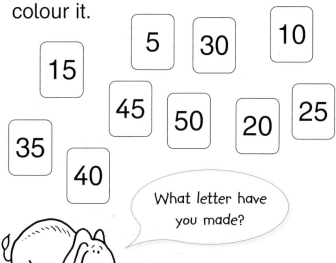

55	10	60	80	15
38	50	34	14	5
65	70	40	12	99
42	90	16	52	85
24	30	20	100	36

What letter have you made?

2 These things are in a sale. Halve the prices.

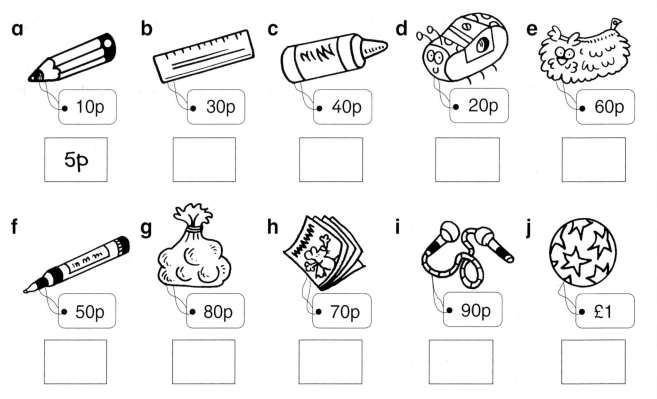

a 10p   5p

b 30p

c 40p

d 20p

e 60p

f 50p

g 80p

h 70p

i 90p

j £1

Estimating and measuring lengths

Name ....

Let's solve problems

1 Estimate, then measure, the distance from the water line to the top of each fish.

Fish	Estimate	Measure
a	_4_ cm	_3_ cm
b	____ cm	____ cm
c	____ cm	____ cm
d	____ cm	____ cm
e	____ cm	____ cm
f	____ cm	____ cm

2 Work with a partner.

You need: the objects in the table below, a ruler, a metre stick.

With your partner, measure and record each object.

Use words like:
• just over • nearly
• just under • about
• almost

Object	Length in cm	Number of objects in 1 metre
straw	14 cm	just over 7
new pencil		
domino		
playing card		
Geostrip		
your foot		
your partner's foot		

Measuring lengths

Name ....

Let's solve problems

1 Write the length of each object to the nearest centimetre.

a

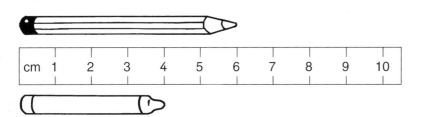

pencil _____ cm

crayon _____ cm

The pencil is _____ cm _____ than the crayon.

b

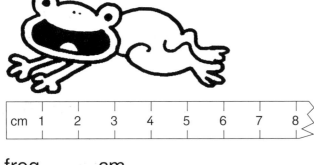

frog _____ cm

mouse _____ cm

The mouse is _____ cm _____ than the frog.

2 Write the height of each dog to the nearest 10 cm.

a 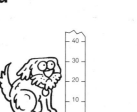 _____ cm

b  _____ cm

c 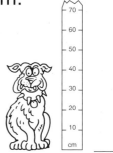 _____ cm

3 Find a way to measure these zig-zag lines.

a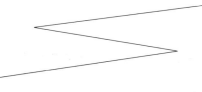

_____ cm long

b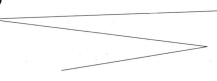

_____ cm long

Estimating and measuring mass

Name ....

Let's solve problems

1 Match each object to the correct label.

lighter than 1kg

heavier than 1kg

2 Work with a partner.

You need: scales, a tea cup, sand, rice, pasta and colouring pencils.

- Estimate first. Then measure.
- Colour the cups to show how many make 1 kilogram.

Estimate　　　　　　　　**Number of cups to make 1 kg**

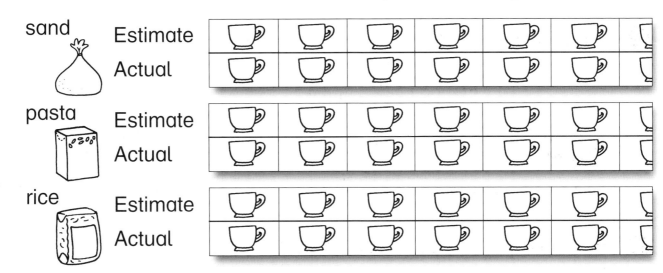

3 Look at your answers to question 2.

a Is 1 cup of sand lighter or heavier than 1 cup of pasta? _____

b Is 1 cup of pasta lighter or heavier than 1 cup of rice? _____

Weighing in kilograms

Name ....

Let's solve problems

1 Write each weight to the nearest kilogram.

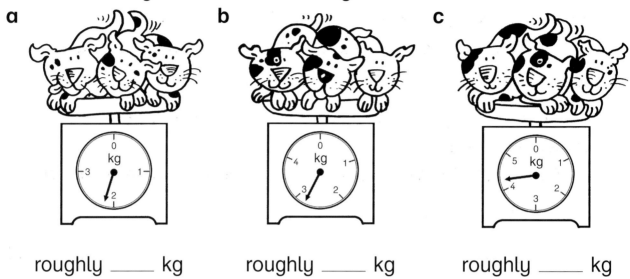

a

b

c

roughly ____ kg   roughly ____ kg   roughly ____ kg

2 Write the weight to the nearest kilogram.

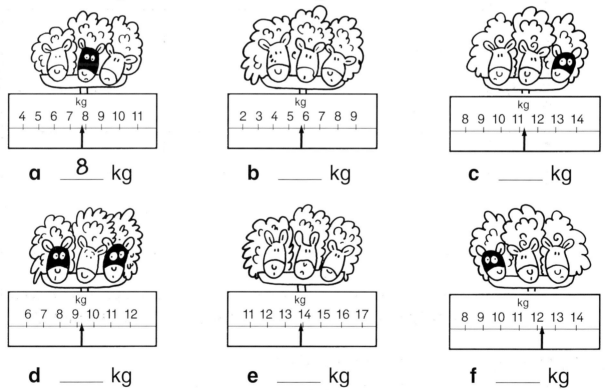

a ___8___ kg

b _____ kg

c _____ kg

d _____ kg

e _____ kg

f _____ kg

3 Order the weights in question 2. Start with the lightest.

sheep __b__ sheep _____ sheep _____ sheep _____ sheep _____ sheep _____

Estimating and measuring capacity

Name ....

Let's investigate

1 Work with a partner.

You need: a 1 litre measuring jar, funnel, water,
3 small containers labelled A, B and C, coloured pencils.

■ Estimate how many fills of each container make 1 litre.

container A _____ container B _____ container C _____

■ Now measure.
Colour the blocks to show how many fills make up 1 litre.

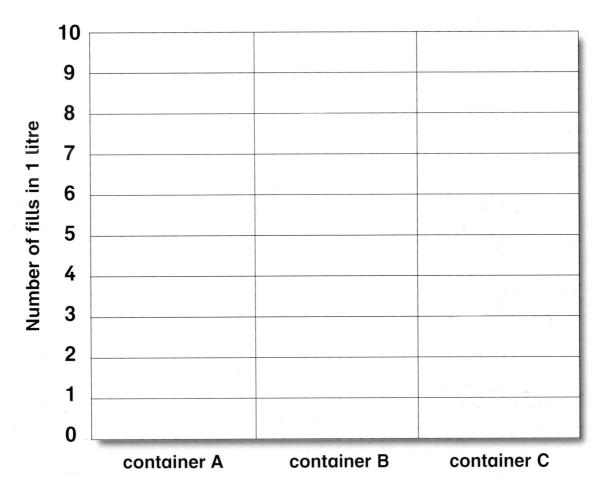

2 Look at your answers to question 1.
One 2 litre bottle of lemonade will give you:

a _____ drinks using container A

b _____ drinks using container B.

Measuring litres in jugs and jars

Name ....

Let's practise

1 Colour the water blue to show the number of litres shown on the label.

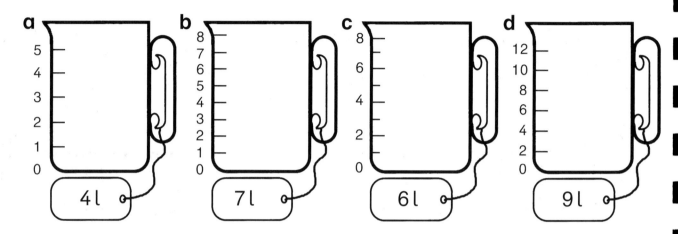

a   4 l   b   7 l   c   6 l   d   9 l

2 Read the level of the water in each jar to the nearest litre.

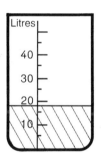

a

just under _____ litres

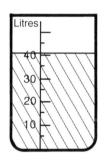

b

just over _____ litres

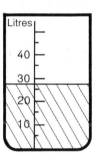

c

less than _____ litres

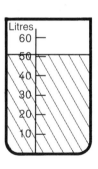

d

just over _____ litres

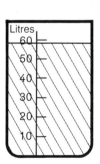

e

nearly _____ litres

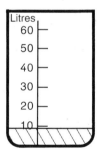

f

about _____ litres

Let's investigate

3 Find a way to work out the weight of 1 litre of water.

Estimating and measuring time

Name ....

Let's practise

1 Draw lines to match the shorts to the T-shirts.

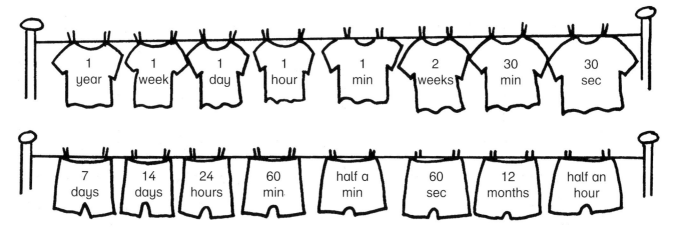

Let's investigate

2 Work with a partner.

In 1 minute I can ...	Estimate	Measure
write my name	_____ times	_____ times
draw round a square	_____ times	_____ times
put pegs on a pegboard	_____ pegs	_____ pegs
build a rod of cubes	_____ cubes	_____ cubes

3 Work with a partner.

You need: a straw each, counters, a paper plate, a 2-minute timer.

- Spread the counters on the table.

Take turns to:

- Suck through the straw.
- Pick up a counter with the straw.
- Drop it on the plate.

How many counters can you put on the plate in 2 minutes? _____

Month by month

Name ....

Let's practise

1 Match the months.

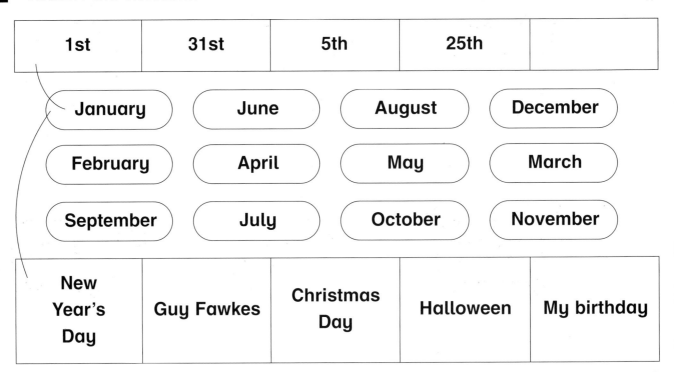

1st	31st	5th	25th	

January June August December

February April May March

September July October November

New Year's Day	Guy Fawkes	Christmas Day	Halloween	My birthday

Let's play   A game for 2

You need: a 1–6 dice,
a dice labelled O, B, O, B, O, B,
a coloured pencil each.

■ Take turns to roll both dice.

■ **O** means **count on**, **B** means **count back**.

■ Starting on January count on or back the number of months shown by the dice.

■ Colour the month you land on on your sheet.

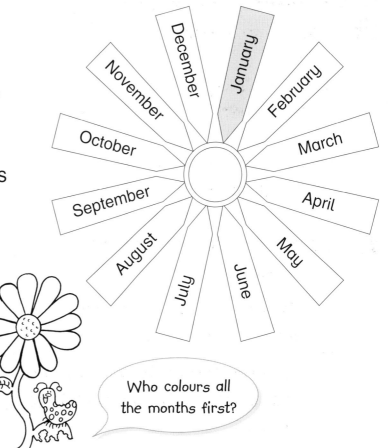

Who colours all the months first?

Reading the time

Name ....

Let's practise

1 Write the times in words.

a

b

c

d

e

f

Let's solve problems

2 Look at this watch.

6:45

a 2 hours ago it showed ⬜ : ⬜

b half an hour ago it showed ⬜ : ⬜

c in 15 minutes it will show ⬜ : ⬜

d in 2 hours it will show ⬜ : ⬜

3 Colour the digital time. Draw the hands on the clock.

a It's earlier than 6 o'clock and later than 2 o'clock

1:15	2:00
3:15	6:15

b It's more than 3 hours after noon and less than 30 minutes before 5 o'clock

2:45	3:30
4:15	4:45

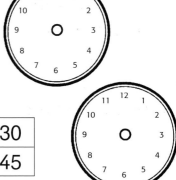

Measuring length problems

Name ....

Let's solve problems

1

The caterpillar crawled 12 m.
It crawled 9 m more.
How far did it crawl altogether?

☐ ☐ ☐ . = ☐ m

2

The fish is 5 cm below the surface. It is 25 cm from the bottom. How deep is the pond?

☐ ☐ ☐ = ☐ cm

3 Sam's flower is
70 cm tall.
Jan's is
14 cm shorter.
How tall is
Jan's flower?

☐ ☐ ☐ = ☐ cm

4 The wall is 8 m high.
The dustbin is 3 m high.
The cat jumps from
the dustbin to the
top of the wall.
How far does
it jump?

☐ ☐ ☐ = ☐ m

5

80 cm

The hedgehog is halfway
between the two plants.
How far has it still to crawl?

☐ ☐ ☐ = ☐ cm

6

12 m

8 m

6 m

The bee flew from the hive to
each flower and back to the
hive.
It flew ☐ m altogether.

Measuring mass problems

Name ....

Let's solve problems

1 Draw lines to match the pets to their weights on the scales.

rabbit	guinea pig	kitten	puppy
•4 kg	•3 kg	•5 kg	•7 kg

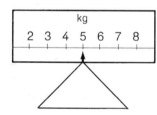 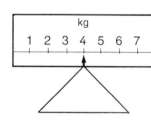 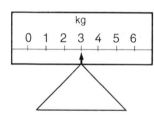 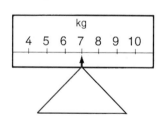

2 **a** The kitten and the puppy weigh ____ kg altogether.

b The rabbit and the guinea pig weigh ____ kg altogether.

c _____ + _____ + _____ together weigh 15 kg.

3 Work out these weights.

a 3 kittens ____ kg **b** 2 puppies ____ kg **c** 4 rabbits ____ kg

4 The rabbit and guinea pig together weigh the same as the _____

Measuring capacity problems

Name ....

Let's solve problems

1 Felix has _____ litres of orange juice.
He pours 1 litre into each small jug.
How many small jugs can he fill?

_____ jugs

2 Ginger has a 1 litre
jug of orange juice.
It fills 4 glasses.

1 litre

    a 2 litres fill _____ glasses.   **b** 3 litres fill _____ glasses.

    c 4 litres fill _____ glasses.   **d** _____ litres fill 20 glasses.

3 Suki has two sizes of orange juice carton.
Find three ways she can measure 5 litres of orange juice.

way 1 [2l] + [2l] + _____

way 2 _____

way 3 _____

4 Panther needs twice as much
orange juice as Suki.
Draw the cartons she opened.

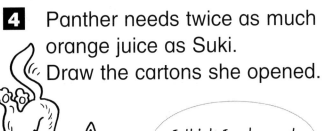

I think I only need
to open 5 cartons.

Time puzzles

Name ....

Let's solve problems

1 Ring the birthdays on the calendar.
   a Hammy   14 July
   b Budge   last Wednesday in July
   c Slither   6 days after Hammy
   d Rex   4 days before Budge

JULY						
Sa	Su	M	T	W	Th	F
1	2	3	4	5	6	7
8	9	10	11	12	13	14
15	16	17	18	19	20	21
22	23	24	25	26	27	28
29	30	31				

2 Write the missing times.

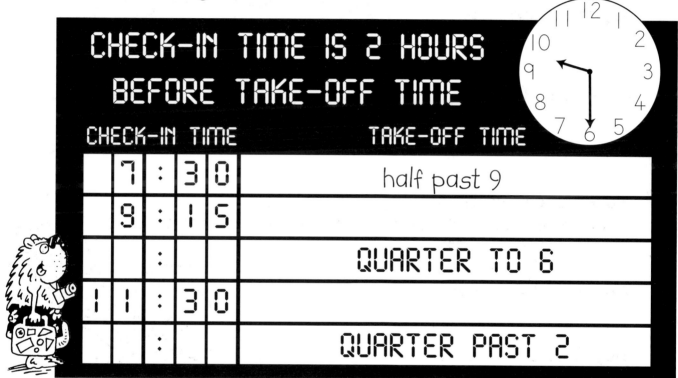

CHECK-IN TIME IS 2 HOURS BEFORE TAKE-OFF TIME

CHECK-IN TIME	TAKE-OFF TIME
7 : 30	half past 9
9 : 15	
:	QUARTER TO 6
11 : 30	
:	QUARTER PAST 2

3 You have 5 digital time cards.
You can use each card only once.
How many different quarter to,
quarter past and half-hour times
can you make?

| 0 | 1 | 3 | 4 | 5 |

3 : 15

Measuring heights

Name ....

Let's solve problems

This climbing wall is 30 metres high.

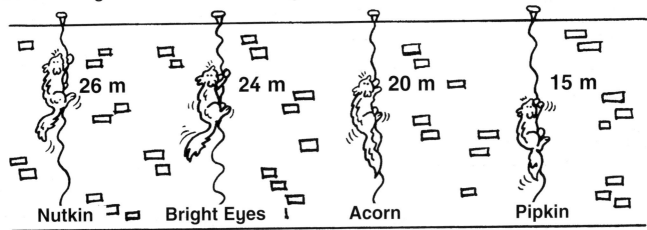

Nutkin 26 m   Bright Eyes 24 m   Acorn 20 m   Pipkin 15 m

1   Complete the table.

	Name	Height climbed	Amount still to climb
a	Nutkin	26 m	_____ m
b	Bright Eyes	24 m	_____ m
c	Acorn	20 m	_____ m
d	Pipkin	15 m	_____ m

2   **a**   Nutkin is _____ m higher than Acorn.

    b   Acorn is _____ m lower than Bright Eyes and

       _____ m higher than Pipkin.

    c   _____ has 10 m still to climb.

    d   _____ has climbed half way.

3

Can you make 5 more lengths by joining 2 lengths of rope?

21 m   24 m   19 m   25 m

$$25\,m + 19\,m = 44\,m$$

Weight puzzles

Name ....

Let's solve problems

A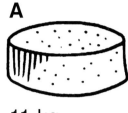
11 kg

B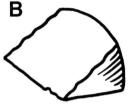
15 kg

C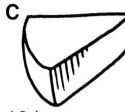
16 kg

D
19 kg

1 **a** Choose 2 cheeses.
Write their total weight.   ____ kg + ____ kg = ____ kg

b Keep choosing cheeses.
Write the totals.

____ kg + ____ kg = ____ kg   ____ kg + ____ kg = ____ kg

____ kg + ____ kg = ____ kg   ____ kg + ____ kg = ____ kg

2 Write the difference in weight between

a cheese A and cheese C   ____ kg − ____ kg = ____ kg

b cheese B and cheese D.   ____ kg − ____ kg = ____ kg

3 A giant buys 3 of cheese B.

The total weight of cheese is ____ kg.

4 A giant buys cheese A.
He cuts off 1 kg for sandwiches.
He cuts the rest of the cheese in half.

Each half weighs ____ kg.

Picture the shape

Name ....

Let's solve problems

1 Make the shape on your pinboard. Draw it in the picture frame.

a 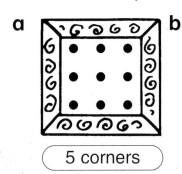   b 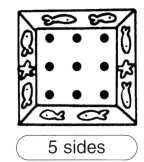   c    d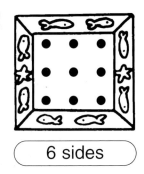

| 5 corners | 5 sides | 6 corners | 6 sides |

2 Draw more lines so that each frame shows an octagon.

a 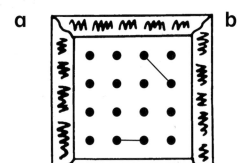   b 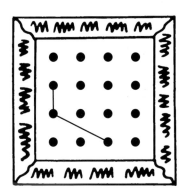   c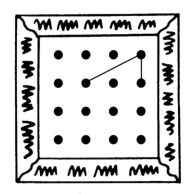

Let's play   A game for 3 or 4

You need: a dice, a supply of straws.

- Take turns to roll the dice.
- Pick up that number of straws.
- Every player takes 5 turns.
- Then make pentagons with your straws.

The winner is the player with the most pentagons.

Solid shapes

Name ....

Let's solve problems

1 Count the shapes.

a cuboids __I__   **b** cones ____

c cylinders ____   **d** pyramids ____

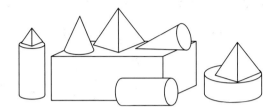

Colour red all the shapes with curved edges.
Colour yellow all the shapes with 4 or more corners.

2 Describe the faces of each shape.

a    _4 rectangles_

2 squares

b 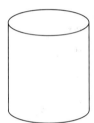   _____

_____

c    _____

_____

d   _____

_____

3 Work with a partner.
You need: a red, a blue and a green pencil.

Draw the shapes in order in the table.
Then colour them. Use these clues.

- The shape with triangular faces is in the middle.
- The shape with 2 circular faces and **2 curved edges** is to the left of the pyramid.
- The green shape is beside the cylinder.
- The cone is not red.
- The blue shape is not the pyramid.

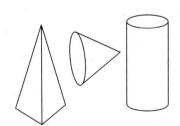

left	middle	right

Line symmetry

Name ....

Let's solve problems

1 Draw the line of symmetry. Use a mirror to check.

a    b    c

2 Colour the pegs to make a pattern with a line of symmetry.

a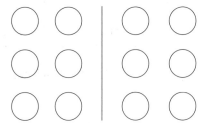

b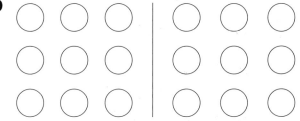

3 Draw a line of symmetry on each flag.

a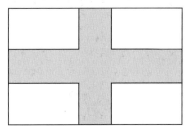

b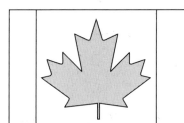

4
■ Trace the frog onto one half of a sheet of paper or card.
■ Fold along the dotted line.
■ Cut out the frog through both layers of paper.
■ Draw the matching eye.

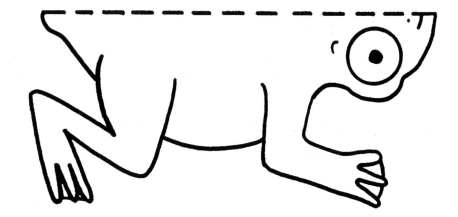

Position

Name ....

Let's solve problems

1 Complete the sentences. | higher than | next to | on the edge of |

    a The is _____ the jigsaw.

    b The are _____ the cap.

    c The is _____ the display box.

2 **a** Draw a  below the .

    b Draw a  between the and the ▢ .

    c Draw some  higher than the and lower than

    the  .

    d Draw a 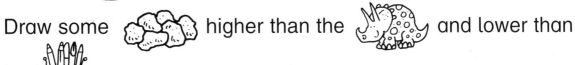 higher than the .

3 Choose an empty box.   The caveman is _____

    Draw a .   _____

                      _____

    Write a clue.   _____

Quarter turns and right angles

Name ....

Let's solve problems

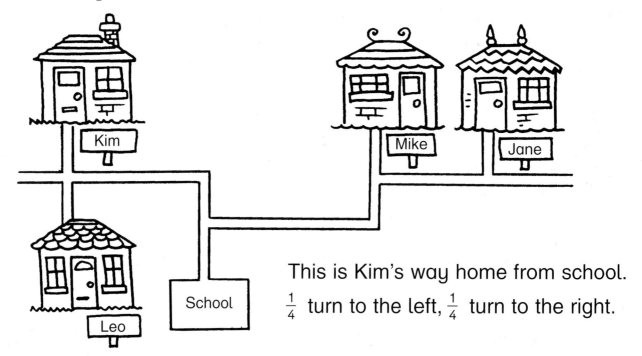

This is Kim's way home from school.
$\frac{1}{4}$ turn to the left, $\frac{1}{4}$ turn to the right.

1 Who follows these routes home?

a $\frac{1}{4}$ turn to the right, $\frac{1}{4}$ turn to the left _____

b $\frac{1}{4}$ turn to the left, $\frac{1}{4}$ turn to the left _____

2 Mark all the right angles in the shapes with a small square.

a 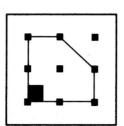 **b** 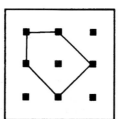 **c** 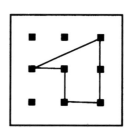 **d**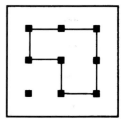

3 Draw the position of the pointer after these turns.

a 1 right angle
   clockwise

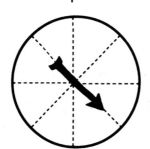

b 1 half turn
   anticlockwise

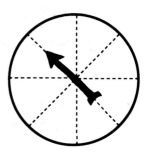

Routes and mazes

Name ....

Let's solve problems

1 The numbers show how many mice are in each room.
Mark the route the cat should take to catch as many mice as possible.

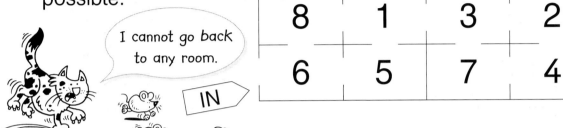

I cannot go back to any room.

IN

8	1	3	2
6	5	7	4

OUT

How many mice did the cat catch? _____

2 The map shows a safe route
for the ship to reach port.
Fill in the sailor's log.

- along 2 squares
- turn left
- up 3 squares
- _____
- _____
- _____
- _____
- _____
- _____

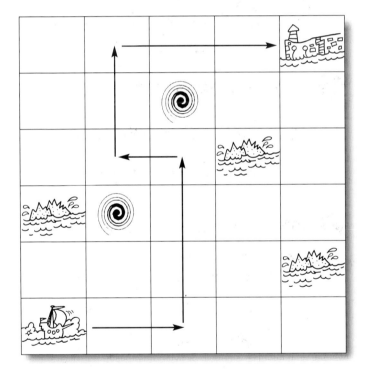

3 Work with a partner.
You need: a counter.

- Place the counter on the ship.
- Give instructions for a different safe route.
- Your partner follows them by moving the counter.
  Can you reach port safely?

Shape puzzles

Name ....

Let's solve problems

1 For each pentagon, draw straight lines to join 1 to 3 and 3 to 5.

a 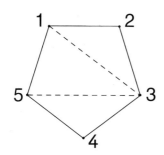   b 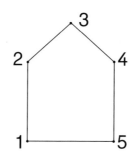   c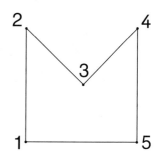

Now count the triangles.

_____ triangles   _____ triangles   _____ triangles

2   **a**   Join the dots. 1 to 2, 2 to 3 and so on.

Name the shape.

_____

b   Now join these dots ⊙

Name the shape.

_____

3   Can you find more than 8 triangles in this shape?

I found _____ triangles.

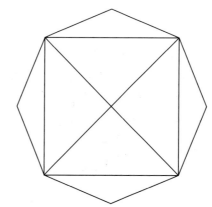

Pictures and patterns

Name ....

Let's solve problems

You need: hexagons and triangles.

1 Use your shapes to make these fish.

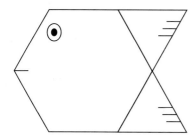 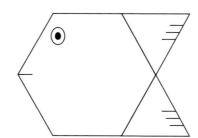 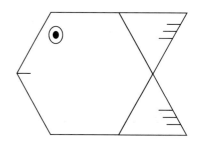

2 Complete the table.

Number of fish	Total number of fins
1	
2	
3	

3 Write about the pattern you see.

_____

_____

_____

_____

4 Use the pattern to complete the table.

Fish	Fins
7	
10	
	40
	50

5 How many fins do you need to make 5 octagon fish?

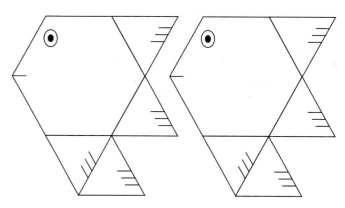

5 octagon fish have _____ fins.

Making a list

Name ....

Let's practise

1 Write each group of numbers in order, smallest first.

a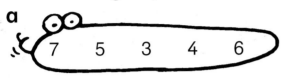
7   5   3   4   6

b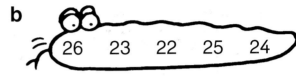
26   23   22   25   24

c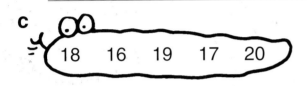
18   16   19   17   20

d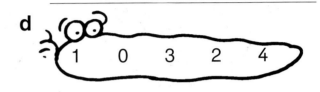
1   0   3   2   4

e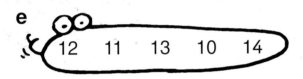
12   11   13   10   14

f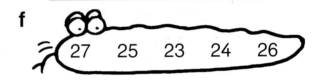
27   25   23   24   26

Let's play   A game for 2

You need: 3 dice, paper and a pencil each.

Take 8 turns each to:
- Roll the 3 dice.
- Find the total of the 3 scores.
- Make a list of your totals.
- You can write each total only once.

> Who has more numbers on their list?

Let's investigate

2 Make lists of:
- the people on your table
- the people in your house
- the teachers in your school.

Compare your lists with a partner.

Using a table

Name ....

Let's practise

1 Split the numbers into tens and units.

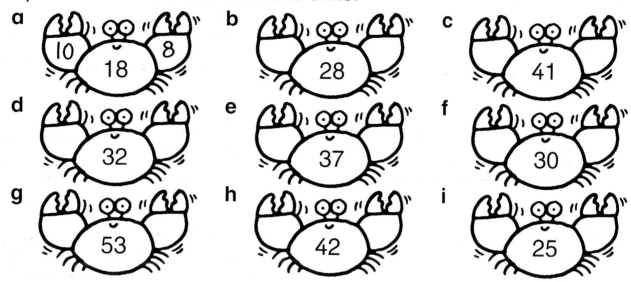

a 10 18 8   b 28   c 41

d 32   e 37   f 30

g 53   h 42   i 25

2 You need: from 1 to 50 number cards:

- Shuffle the cards and take 20.
- Write your numbers in the correct place in the table.

Numbers up to 10	Numbers from 11 to 20	Numbers from 21 to 30	Numbers from 31 to 40	Numbers from 41 to 50

Let's solve problems

3 Look at the numbers that were split in question 1.

    a Write them in the table, using a red pencil.

    b Which number does not fit? _____

4 Write 2 extra numbers in each part of the table, using a blue pencil.

Tallying

Name ....

Let's practise

1 Write these numbers as tallies.

   a 6   **b** 12   **c** 21   **d** 14

   e 16   **f** 15   **g** 18   **h** 19

2 Write the numbers that these tallies show.

  a ‖‖‖ ||| ____ **b** ‖‖‖ ‖‖‖ ||\ ____ **c** ‖‖‖ ‖‖‖ ||\\ ____ **d** |\ ____

  e ‖‖‖ \ ____ **f** ‖‖‖ ‖‖‖ ____ **g** ‖‖‖ ‖‖‖ ‖‖‖\ ____ **h** ‖‖‖ ____

Let's play An activity for 3

You need: a 1-minute timer.

- Number yourselves 1, 2 and 3.
- Child 1 watches child 2.
- Child 2 watches the timer.
- Child 1 says 'Blink' every time child 2 blinks.
- Child 3 keeps a tally.
- Stop counting when the timer stops.
- Swap jobs and repeat.

Name	Number of blinks

Making a pictogram

Name ....

Let's investigate An activity for 2

You need: scissors, glue, sheet of blank paper.

- Find out how many brothers and sisters your classmates have.
- Cut out the faces.
- Use one for each classmate.
- Stick it on the pictogram to show how many brothers and sisters they have.

0	**1**	**2**	**3**	**4**	**more than 4**

Number of brothers and sisters

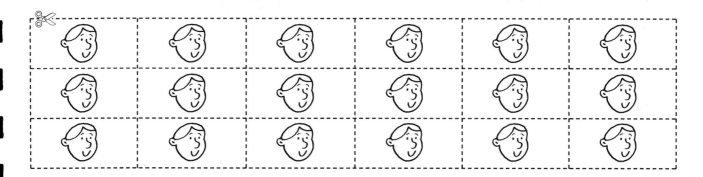

Sorting money

Name ....

Let's investigate   An activity for 2

You need: lots of coins.

- Take a handful of coins each.
- Place them on the grid to make a pictogram.

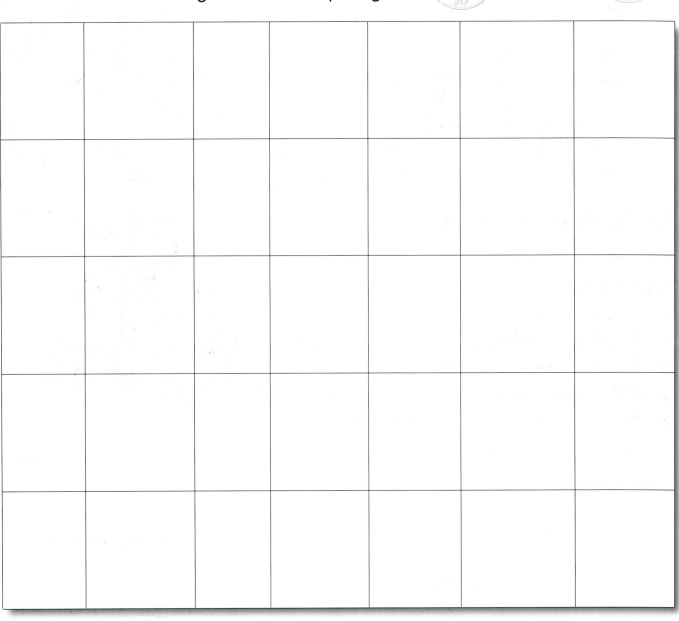

1p	2p	5p	10p	20p	50p	£1

- Compare your pictogram with your partner's.
- Discuss what is the same.
- Discuss what is different.

Maths Spotlight 1. Copying permitted for purchasing school only. This material is not copyright free.

Guess my rule

Name ....

Let's practise

1 Colour the numbers that are both less than 50 and odd.

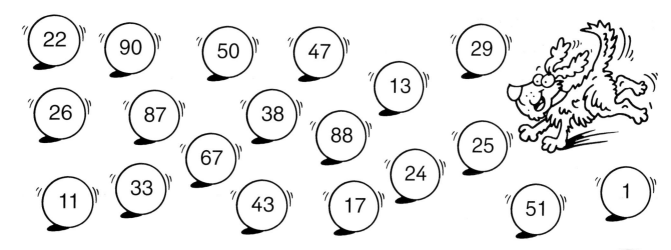

22　90　50　47　29

26　87　38　13

67　88　25

11　33　24

43　17　51　1

Let's play　A game for 2

You need: number cards from 0 to 20, a set ring.

Take turns to:

- Choose a rule from the box.
- Find the number cards that fit the rule.
- Put them inside the ring.
- Put the rest of the numbers outside the ring.
- Your partner guesses which rule you chose.

Ends in 3

3　13

Rules

Is less than 12

Is odd numbers

Is greater than 15

Has 1 ten

Is even numbers

Is between 10 and 15

Ends in 3

Has 9 units

Making a block graph

Name ....

Let's investigate

1 Look at the shoes of your classmates.
Colour one square for each child.

Shoes in our class

a Which is the most popular type of shoe? _____

b Which is the least popular type of shoe? _____

c Find the difference between the number of
lace-up shoes and the number of velcro shoes. _____

2 Write 2 sentences about your graph.

_____

_____